Advances in Psychology Series

MODELS OF THINKING

F. H. GEORGE

Brunel University
and Bureau of Information Science

Models of Thinking

London

GEORGE ALLEN AND UNWIN LTD

RUSKIN HOUSE · MUSEUM STREET

FIRST PUBLISHED IN 1970

© *George Allen & Unwin Ltd.*, 1970

SBN 04 153004 7 *cloth*
SBN 04 153005 5 *paper*

PRINTED IN GREAT BRITAIN
in 10 on 12 pt. Times
BY WILLMER BROTHERS LIMITED
BIRKENHEAD

For Clare and Karen

FOREWORD

This book has been written over a period of nearly three years so I am aware that a certain amount of research has occurred during its writing which has not been sufficiently absorbed by me to include in the text. This is inevitable and both the writer and the reader must accept this fact.

One other point is the use of quotation marks. Single quotation marks are used to indicate *words*, rather than their referents. Double quotation marks are used to emphasize a degree of vagueness in a word or phrase, as well as an actual quotation. Italics are used for emphasis.

I would like to acknowledge my indebtedness to Professor John Cohen for his help throughout the whole project and his assistant Mr. E. I. Chesnick for the most detailed analysis of the text and the most helpful suggestions.

F. H. GEORGE
Bristol, 1969

CONTENTS

CONTENTS

PART ONE

COGNITION

The first part of this monograph provides a background to problems of thinking. We shall try to say a little bit, mostly by a jog of the elbow as a reminder, about previous ideas on the subject. These ideas have come mainly from psychologists and philosophers, and the emphasis is a little more on theory than on experiment, although both are recognized as being vital.

We are also trying to define, or redefine, some familiar terms from the field of cognition, and in Chapter 1 we discuss briefly our methods. An attitude to perception and to cognition generally is indicated but little more, and all of this is meant to provide a broad context into which the more precise work of Part II fits. These more precise models are of some aspects of cognition, and the aim is to put them together to give a precise and coherent "starting" model of cognition.

Introduction

This book aims to describe an approach to thinking and problem-solving. It is a research undertaking based on the assumption that descriptive precision and formalization is a complementary approach to the existing studies of the central cognitive processes. It is complementary to, and not inconsistent with, an approach by philosophers, psychologists and physiologists, but is itself based on the methods usually associated with workers in the field of artificial intelligence.

The danger of this approach is that one may ignore, as a result of the search for precision, the subtleties already unearthed by researchers in the disciplines referred to above. Unwittingly we may present rigorous but oversimplified models and theories, and as a result the work will either be ignored as inept or rendered much less useful than one might hope.

It is accepted from the start that the approach followed here is knowingly oversimplified in the interests of methodological precision. It is recognized that we are using formal models to simulate human-like systems, although not necessarily fully achieving that object at the first attempt. For example, we shall talk of Markov Chains, Bayesian decisions, inverse probability and the like. These are clearly sophisticated methods which could hardly be said to be normally used, certainly not in any conscious or explicit sense, by a human thinker while attempting to solve a problem or make a decision. However, it is nevertheless possible that such methods provide a description of the structure or function of the nervous system if indeed that is where thinking occurs.

We shall not in this monograph deal with the nervous system as such, but only with molar models of cognitive behaviour. At the same time our models will try to anticipate the ultimate comparison with actual neural structures.

We have no wish to introduce mathematical terminology needlessly, but we do use some algebraic and logical symbols borrowed from the Propositional Calculus, the Functional Calculi and the Calculus of Relations. We collect these terms together and list most of them in appendix 3.

Guthrie[1] claimed that all cognitive problems are based on conditioning, and Thorndike[2] claimed that what he called 'the principle of association' is sufficient to explain the whole of thinking and problem solving. Thorndike himself however frequently referred to ideational learning and problem solving.

In the background of the subject, one is reminded of the traditional division of thinking into reasoning and imagination; our effort is concentrated mainly on the first. The notions of discovery and invention may involve both, but we are here primarily concerned with the more logical types of process. We are concerned with the ability to abstract, with the development of concepts, and with all the features that have long been regarded as central to thinking by experimental and theoretical psychologists. Thought as studied introspectively (e.g. by the Würzburg school), thought and muscular activity[3] and 'silent speech', as well as the many studies of concept formation in children,[4] Ruger's puzzles[5] and adult hypothesising[6] are all features, like many others not mentioned, which will be borne in mind, even if they are 'taken as read' and not, in the main, explicitly discussed.

The first major contribution to an understanding of thinking

1 E. R. Guthrie, *The Psychology of Learning*, New York: Harper, 1935.

2 E. L. Thorndike, *The Fundamentals of Learning*, New York: Teachers College, 1932.

3 L. W. Max, An experimental study of the motor theory of consciousness: III. Action-current responses in deaf mutes during sleep, sensory stimulation and dreams. *J. Comp. Psychol.*, 1935, *19*, 469–86.

L. W. Max, An experimental study of the motor theory of consciousness: IV. Action-current responses in the deaf during awakening, kinaesthetic imagery and abstract thinking. *J. Comp. Psychol.*, 1937, *24*, 301–44.

4 J. Piaget, *Judgement and Reasoning in the Child*, New York: Harcourt Brace, 1928.

5 H. A. Ruger, The psychology of efficiency; an experimental study of the process involved in the solution of mechanical puzzles and in the acquisition of skill in their manipulation. *Arch. Psychol.*, 1910, New York, *2*, 15.

6 E. Claparède, La genèse de l'hypothèse, *Arch. de Psychol.*, 1933, *24*, 1–154.

came in an associationist type of theory, which was thought in essence to explain the whole of so-called 'mental life'. Humphrey[1] summarizes typical associationist views in the following terms:

'To sum up, it may be said that the associational theory, where it stands by its own principles, represents all mental events, simple or complex, as collocations of generically unchanged elements resulting from the elementary stimulation of the organism.'

Humphrey goes on to liken such a view to that of the atomic theory and its use, and he reminds us of the great success of the atomic principle in the physical sciences.

Conditioning theory is basic to what we might call 'Naive Associationism'. Pavlov and Watson immediately come to mind as initiators in some part, and supporters in some part, of Naive Associationism.

There is no purpose to be served in this book by stating the various alternative behaviouristic theories.[2,3,4] But we should point out two major features at least, which suggest that such Naive Associationism is not sufficient to provide explanations at the level of human thinking. The first of these factors is that it has not been possible to show that learning theories of even the more sophisticated behaviouristic kind (e.g. Tolman) can account for thinking.

As Hunt[5] says, "No simple universally accepted learning system exists". He goes on to say that there are a vast number of different interpretations that can be placed on so-called S-R (stimulus-response) theories and on the very nature of S-R associations. Habit strength, which is one of Hull's[2] basic variables and supposedly measures the strength of such S-R connections, does not seem to vary continuously as Hull supposed. Furthermore, many other of the concepts used by him and other S-R theorists do not satisfactorily explain all the experimental evidence.

Far more serious from our point of view than the existence of various doubts about particular learning theories is the second factor that such theories are not apparently sophisticated enough to

[1] G. Humphrey, *Thinking*, London: Methuen, 1951.

[2] C. L. Hull, *A Behaviour System: an Introduction to Behaviour Theory concerning the Individual Organism*, Yale University Press, 1952.

[3] E. C. Tolman, A cognition motivation model *Psychol. Rev.*, 1952, 59, 389–400.

[4] B. F. Skinner, *The Behaviour of Organisms: an Experimental Analysis*, New York: Appleton-Century-Crofts, 1938.

[5] E. B. Hunt, *Concept Learning: an information processing problem*, New York: Wiley, 1962.

B

account for human thinking nor do they even provide a suitable framework for it. Hunt puts the whole matter succinctly:

'Learning theorists had originally hoped to devise a concept-learning model which treated complex categorizations as a specialization of discrimination learning. This proved impossible. Some form of mediating response had to be introduced into the analysis of concept learning in the human adult.'

Mediation hypotheses have not in turn been completely successful but they do form a link with the most up-to-date theories of learning which come nearer to explaining the use of concepts and hypotheses and their formation in human thinking and problem solving. This at least takes us past Naive Associationism, and we shall discuss what we might call Sophisticated or Critical Associationism in another section. Before we do so, however, let us briefly look at the alternatives to associationism.

Langfeld, Boring and Weld[1] pointed out, as did many others, the need to support a contiguity theory, which is typically associationist, by a selective process such as motivation.

'Set'[2] is a word that is well known for its ambiguity, but *Aufgabe*, as used by Watt[3] and Ach[4] is certainly concerned with a central aspect of what we mean. If you are hungry you are motivated to find food and eat it until, with satiation, the need for food has gone. Set is an alerting or selecting system that at any particular time makes us more sensitive to certain events rather than to others. No doubt it derives from a motivated state such as the occurring of a need, but its positive role in *actively* relating the organism to its environment is precisely what is missing from the early associationist theories. Organisms are dynamic, goal-seeking systems that manipulate and change their environment and are not merely passive victims of it.

Some writers have almost equated thinking with reasoning but we shall here distinguish between them. Reasoning, we shall say is a

---

[1] E. G. Boring, H. S. Langfeld and H. P. Weld, *Foundations of Psychology* New York: Wiley, 1948.

[2] J. J. Gibson, A critical review of the concept of set in contemporary experimental psychology. *Psychol. Bull.*, 1941, *38*, 781–817.

[3] H. J. Watt, *Experimentelle Beitrage zueiner Theories des Denkens. Arch. ges. Psychol.*, 1905, *4*, 289–436.

[4] N. Ach, *Über die Willenstätigheit und das Denken*, Gottingen: Vandenhoeck and Ruprecht, 1905.

part of thinking. In thinking, we sometimes freely associate and perform other operations such as data retrieval, which is not in itself reasoning so the word "thinking" seems to be used to include more than reasoning. But doubtless different people use words in different ways.

The Würzburg School, whose work was essentially experimental in its approach, showed the importance of *motive* and *set* to thought. Külpe, in particular, emphasised the need for intermediate presentations, or models, from which thought occurs. Imageless thought was also one of their cornerstones, but whereas it can be accepted that not all thought is connected directly to sensation, it would be difficult to accept the notion that thought does not often, even usually, involve imaging.

The largest single school concerned with thinking which was essentially anti-associationist in its whole approach, is represented by Gestalt theory. Gestalt theorists were, above all, anti-associationist. They held a highly critical view of Naive Associationism and were much more obviously opposed to it than, say, the Würzburg School. Sound thinking, they argued, is "productive" not "reproductive". The so-called law of Prägnanz suggests a directing of percepts and concepts towards the "good". "Good" here means regular, simple, stable, etc. This belief is lacking in sufficient experimental support, but there is some evidence that, when we think, we both recombine old and construct new concepts and hypotheses. Furthermore, there is no doubt that in memory we simplify information and often omit detail.

It is doubtful whether many people today would accept the Gestalt views; at best they may accept that the theory has underlined difficulties for naive or even critical associationism, but offered no complete or acceptable alternative.

The Gestalt School say of problem solving and thinking that such activities are initiated by problems; this we can agree with. They further assert that stresses are set up by the problem which are alleviated by "organic activity". Such organic activity is exemplified for example by a dog searching for food, but, of course, we are interested in the higher level processes that provide or attempt to provide the problem's solution. Here Wertheimer[1] and Maier[2]—

1 M. Wertheimer, *Productive thinking*, New York: Harper, 1945.
2 N. R. F. Maier, The bevahiour mechanisms concerned with problem solving. *Psychol. Rev.*, 1940, *47*, 43–58.

the latter is not a wholehearted Gestaltist—discuss some of the details of the inhibiting "natural" responses as one of many conditions for satisfactory problem solving, and again we may accept this as relevant. In general, Gestaltists have emphasised the integration or construction of *wholes* from their constituent parts as a necessary condition for problem solving.

We shall say no more about the work of Gestalt psychology. We shall try to remember some of their followers injunctions, but will not attempt to follow Gestalt theory itself.

More recent approaches to thinking include the work of the factor analysts[1] who have examined "the structure of intellect", as they would put it. They claim to have discovered more than fifty different intellectual factors and these can be classified in three fundamental ways. One of these ways is to divide factors up in terms of the kind of processes involved. These include divergent production (or Induction) and cognition and evaluation. The second way is in terms of the products of thought e.g. units, classes, relations, etc., and the third way deals with kinds of contents such as figural, symbolic and semantic.

The above work resembles that which is based on information processing, and is thus very similar in outlook to the view to be taken in this monograph. It is also closely related to the outlook of workers in the field of artificial intelligence such as Newell, Shaw and Simon, Gelerntner, Feigenbaum, Samuel and others, who provide a starting point for the work described in this book.

Hunt, perhaps, more than any other single person, is in the position of linking this last group working in the field of artificial intelligence with the psychologists working on theories of thinking. We shall try to effect a similar link.

In other words, we may accept that there are many possible approaches to the problem of thinking and no one that is obviously valid at the expense of the others. The view expressed in this monograph is essentially critically realistic (we hope highly critical) and essentially of the information-processing kind.

[1] H. H. Harmon, *Modern Factor Analysis*, Chicago: University of Chicago Press, 1960.

1

Methods in Cognition

---

1 A Starting Point

We could not hope, as we have already said, to do justice to all aspects and approaches to human thinking in one short monograph, but we must say something more of our aims and methods.

In writing this brief account of an approach to thinking, we have constantly been aware of Wittgenstein's[1] well-known criticism of experimental psychology:

'The confusion and barrenness of psychology is not to be explained by calling it a "young science"; its state is not comparable with that of physics, for instance, in its beginnings. (Rather with that of certain branches of mathematics. Set theory.) For in psychology there are experimental methods and *conceptual confusion*. (As in the other case conceptual confusion and methods of proof.)

The existence of experimental methods makes us think we have the means of solving the problems which trouble us; though problem and methods pass one another by.'

This criticism of experimental psychology, at the time it was made, seemed to the present writer to be almost entirely justified. Experimental psychologists were, at that time, struggling to unscramble their concepts and clarify their language and models: at worst they believed that as long as a well-controlled experiment was carried out, the mere accumulation of facts would make a science. The relation, so vital to the development of psychology, between experimental

---

1 L. Wittgenstein, *Philosophical Investigations*, Oxford. Blackwell, 1953.

results, by way of interpretation, and explanatory frameworks, models, etc, used largely to be neglected.

In fact, much of this conceptual confusion has now disappeared. Almost everyone now acknowledges that theory and experiment, model making, theory construction and linguistics all go together, and that the successful development of a science of behaviour depends upon a 'total approach' and not a narrow one-sided one, whether narrowly experimental or narrow in any other way.

The account that follows of thinking, and the closely allied cognitive processes, is based on at least the following assumptions:

1 We must be reasonably clear, in our prior linguistic analysis of the problem, as to what we are searching for, what methods are appropriate to our search, and in what precise context we are working.

2 We need to construct models, and thus theories, which are as precise as possible, and capable of being tested.

3 Since the digital computer is the only large-scale universal model, we may expect to follow the prescription of Simon[1] and construct our models—or most of them—in the form of computer programs.

4 The need for a computer to be used as the main tool is simply because its size and speed are needed to handle the ultimate size and complexity of the necessary model. The model itself needs as a result of using the computer, to be formal, and we have to be prepared for the criticisms of those who seem to believe that some of the higher level 'mental' operations are not formalizable[2].

5 We naturally need to be familiar with what has been discovered already and its probable relevance to the present search.

6 We must certainly try to establish a viewpoint regarding related matters such as *consciousness* and *imaging*, otherwise the context in which our model will fit will still be unclear, and therefore its usefulness will be reduced.

7 We accept the fact that our efforts are essentially behaviouristic, and it is to be hoped that this will not be of a narrow kind, nor rule out the need to discuss consciousness, imaging and the like; a highly critical form of associationism is, as we have said, what we hope to achieve.

---

[1] H. A. Simon, *Models of Man*, New York: Wiley, 1957.
[2] H. L. Dreyfus, *Alchemy and Artificial Intelligence*, Rand Memo, p. 3244, 1965.

8 Finally, we must try to refine our ideas as we go along and as new models become available and are tested. *We need a continuous monitoring process, which has no obvious ending, but hopefully improves our prediction and understanding by stages.*

We are, some people would say, taking a *cybernetic* approach to our subject. The fact is that we are using a digital computer at some stage (or stages) to construct models, and as a result we are necessarily looking for formalized models, and one can call this procedure 'cybernetic' or not according to choice.

The use of the words 'theory' and 'model' deserves some mention. They are interchangeable in general, but are relative to each other *in a context.* So like Braithwaite[1] we shall think of theories as *interpretations* of models, and models as *formalizations* of theories. For example, Fitch and Barry[2] provided a model for Hull's first theory of learning, and the Propositional Calculus is an interpretation of the same model as is interpreted as the Calculus of Classes.

2 Simulation and Synthesis

We next deal with the problem of models which are *syntheses* as opposed to those which are *simulations*. As usual, the difference is one of degree, and not absolute.

By the *synthesis* of a system, such as in the form of an artificially intelligent system, we shall mean a model capable of producing intelligent behaviour of one kind or another, without any pretence that the *methods* used bear any necessary resemblance to those used by human beings. *Simulation*, on the other hand, which is a particular case of synthesis, not only attempts to achieve the same ends, but also claims to produce them in a way which is similar to the way they are carried out by human beings. Indeed simulation is concerned with producing what is somewhat less than a perfectly reliable intelligent system, in keeping with the unreliabilities observed in human behaviour.

We are, in this book, interested mainly in simulation, but there is, of course, no assumption that the simulation models we are going

[1] R. B. Braithwaite, *Scientific Explanation*, London: Cambridge University Press, 1953.
[2] F. B. Fitch and G. Barry, Towards a Formalization of Hull's Behaviour Theory, 1950, *Phil. Sci., 17*, 260–5.

to discuss are constructed of the same fabrics as are human beings—
this is another problem again—and we are going to talk only of
simulation *methods*. In fact, there is a sense, as we shall see, in which
our interests lie *between* synthesis and simulation.

We can envisage conveniently, possibly in computer program form,
a large set of automata working on a closed loop principle (i.e.
capable of self-correction) with a very large storage capacity. We
are concerned with the principles of programming and self-programming that are used to promote the behaviour of an automaton; this
is a dynamic closed loop model[1] in a social environment. Given
that the environment bears some resemblance to the human environment, our task is to show that the behaviour of the model bears some
resemblance to that of human beings. We may, of course, expect to
proceed in stages to try to solve this problem, starting, in general,
with the simpler models and gradually moving towards the more
complex (or more detailed) model which bears a close resemblance
to human behaviour.

Although this book is concerned with, and constructed mainly
around, programs written for the digital computer, it should be said
that many other modelling techniques have been used in
tackling these sort of problems. We should particularly mention
neural or logical nets, as well as purely mathematical or mathematical-
logical models. And although the present author has no great
experience of hardware models, it should be borne in mind that,
particularly during the earlier stages of development of these
simulation methods, hardware models of the simpler sorts of
adaptive behaviour were often constructed[2,3]. Furthermore, a
great deal of knowledge has been acquired both by rumination and
experimentation, and we hope to make use of such knowledge.

3 Cognition

Taking a broad view of cognition, our input-output automaton
must be capable of simulating at least the properties of *perception*,
recognition, *recall*, *conceptualizing*, *inference-making*, *problem solving*,
thinking and the use of *language*. It will also be borne in mind

[1] F. H. George, The current state of artificial intelligence, a paper read at the
N.A.T.O. conference on artificial intelligence, Paris, 1967.
[2] W. R. Ashby, *Design for a Brain*, London: Chapman and Hall, 1952.
[3] W. G. Walter, *The Living Brain*, London: Duckworth, 1953.

throughout that the terms used above do not refer to wholly independent properties or mechanisms of the human being. In fact, they
are to be thought of as crude and approximate overlapping labels
for complicated processes. This means that, whereas we might be
able to give a sufficiently precise contextual definition to words like
'conception' or 'learning', we would not necessarily wish to be forced
to adhere to such definitions when constructing the system *as a whole*.
It is in this sense that our undertaking is, as it always should be in
science, contextually defined; its object is to refine our ideas about
human thinking and improve our models at the same time.

We should mention that whilst we think of any scientific investi-
gation as serving a specific purpose in a specific context, this would
not necessarily rule out descriptions, analyses and explanations at
various levels of abstraction.[1]

It is necessary to be aware of what philosophers, logicians,
psychologists, physiologists, ethologists, cyberneticians, etc. have to
say about these matters, whilst our context will help us to decide
whether any specific proposition is relevant or not to our purpose.

4 Thinking

The main problem on which this book will concentrate is that of
thinking and to some extent such related matters as learning and
problem solving which overlap it, and to this end relatively little
will be said about other activities such as perception. But in accor-
dance with the principle stated above, and in the light of a great deal
of psychological experimentation, it seems likely that we cannot
wholly understand thinking and problem solving activity and the
allied fields of learning, without having some knowledge of how
information is received (as well as recognized and recalled) in the
first place. So a chapter will be devoted to a brief statement of an
attitude to human perception.

This section on perception will intentionally be couched in general
terms. At the same time because of the importance and likely
relevance of so-called *perceptual learning*, we shall pay particular
attention to this topic. In other words, partly by our definition of
'perception' and partly by the complex interconnected nature of our

1 R. Crawshay-Williams, *Methods and Criteria of Reasoning*, London: Routledge
and Kegan Paul, 1957.

problem, we might miss much which is vital if we concentrated only on conceptual as opposed to perceptual processes.

In this chapter we have used words such as 'behaviouristic', 'ideas', and the like and we are presuming that these are sufficiently understood. By 'behaviouristic' we mean to convey that the study is objective, or that it is carried out in non-introspective terms. By this we mean that such concepts as *introspection*, *consciousness*, etc, must be explained in terms of what is publicly observable rather than private. Ideas are events which we are aware of privately, but which we assume can be described publicly; ideas are like concepts, and they may refer to events which have not, or could not, occur, as well as those which have.

Our problem will always in part be that of refining our ideas at some point at the expense of other ideas at another related point. We then return and clarify these other ideas, and so we go on defining our terms and redefining them, as much as is needed for some specific contextually defined purpose.

Our method is essentially "hypothetico-deductive" and by that we mean that we formulate hypotheses by induction, test them usually using deduction, and reformulate the hypotheses as necessary.

2

Learning, Problem Solving and Thinking

1 Definitions

In this chapter we must try to clarify our ideas further about the cognitive terms we shall use. We must also go some way to clarifying the relation between such terms as 'learning' and 'perception', and both of these and their relation to 'problem solving' and 'thinking'; we shall try to describe the processes involved, as well as the terms used.

Perception can be thought of, in general terms, as the total process of receiving information, from either the external or the internal environment. 'External' and 'internal' here mean with respect to the body itself, and we can think of 'I' as being a part of the body, almost certainly closely associated with the nervous system. Perception is closely allied to *recognition* and *recall*, and these are parts (in fact major parts) of the process of perception.

Learning we shall define as the process of adapting to changing circumstances and the recording of success and failure in the process. This means that we envisage a system which has the necessary flexibility to adapt to a change in the environment, although we would also wish to distinguish between adaptation which is built in (instinctive, innate) from that which is acquired as a result of transactions between the organism and environment. 'Learning' is, in fact, a term normally applied to the latter category although, of course, we have a practical problem in distinguishing one from the other. We can, however, say that without storing information gained from adaptive processes in action, learning would not be possible.

We might also wish to argue that learning must lead to some sort of reduction in need, but this is not essential to our purpose.

Thinking is the process which we can regard initially as that of symbolizing events and then manipulating the symbols themselves by various processes of logical (and illogical) inference, where the processing—a form of data-processing—may be accompanied by imagery. We shall think of *imagery* as the resuscitation of an input system in a diminished form at some time after the original input took place. In fact, of course, we can think of *imagination* as rather more than this process of imaging, since imagination may combine various previous inputs into a pattern which has never, in actuality, previously occurred.

Problem solving we can think of as the process of acquiring an appropriate set of responses to a "new" situation. The appropriateness of a response to a stimulus, or a stimulus complex, must also depend on motivation. We are, as adaptive and problem solving organisms, motivated to respond to our environment and to achieve goals. The major goal for the human species is presumably that of survival, and responses to *primary motivators*, as we might call them, are processes such as eating when hungry, drinking when thirsty, and the satisfaction of other basic needs such as sex, curiosity, etc. It has been assumed that goals imply sub-goals, and furthermore the achievement of goals leads, by association, to the need to achieve secondary goals or secondary sources of satisfaction. Identification of sub-goals can be carried out deductively; if x is a goal and x implies y, y is a sub-goal.

We may try to clarify this rather complicated situation from another point of view by saying that human beings have purposes, some of which are long term, and some of which are relatively short term, and some of which are very short term. These purposes represent goal-seeking activity, and this implies goals and sub-goals, where sub-goals imply sub-purposes. It is selective reinforcement, where satisfaction stems from the achievement of goals and sub-goals and dissatisfaction springs from the failure to achieve these goals and sub-goals, that is basic and quite necessary to intelligent behaviour.

It is against this background that we have to view thinking and problem solving as a complex behavioural activity. The organism is already thought to perceive, recognize and recall information.

2 The Central Problem

The problem now is the central organization or central processing of the input data, which demands that problem solving should occur. Following our general policy of proceeding by degrees, we shall attempt to envisage a problem solving activity of a reasonably realistic kind, which nevertheless does not involve any sort of 'emotional contamination'.

There are, in fact, broadly speaking, two types of problem that we want to consider. One is of the sequential kind (on-line, in equivalent computer terminology) where a series of events occurs in time and where information at any time may be incomplete, and material where information may never, in some cases, be complete. An appropriate response may occur which achieves the goal of optimizing,[1] say, certain features of that sequence.

Alternatively, the problem may be in the form of a symbolic description where the information will normally be complete (off-line, in computer terms) where a specific solution may be arrived at. In fact, whether the problem is a symbolic one or a non-symbolic one, or whether the solution to the problem is arrived at by a precise and determinate process or is a probabilistic one and arrived at by an optimizing process, is not of fundamental importance. The fact of the matter is that there are various problems which we shall call sequential and are either 'on-going' or completed and come under this general heading.

We can, of course, further distinguish differences between the types of problems and types of solution much more finely than we have done so far, but there is no point, for our limited purpose, in doing so. One of the second type of problems that occur is where the problem itself is precisely to know what the problem is. In these circumstances, it is the search to understand the problem, usually in the light of knowing that goal-seeking activities are not as yet being carried out effectively that is the problem.

In general, this second type of problem is not one which is sequential in time, but is nevertheless a definite puzzle involving a collection of items, which may in turn reduce to one which is sequential in time by virtue of the way the human organism scans the puzzle. But the

1 F. H. George, Formation and analysis of concepts and hypotheses on a digital computer. *J. Math. Biosciences*, 1968. (In press)

scanning of a puzzle, which is fixed, is one such as the scanning of a chess board at any particular instant of time where the problem is to decide what next move is required; this is, in some sense, non-sequential. In the same way a crossword puzzle which demands a synonym, or the solution to a particular verbal question, although it may be tackled as a process which is sequential in time, is not in and of itself sequential. This distinction, as we have said is much the same as what is called 'on-line' (sequential) or 'off-line' (non-sequential) in computer terms. They are two aspects of the same problem, and one occurs (necessarily) in real time and the other *may* occur at leisure. The difference may be put simply. In one case we are trying to solve a problem where evidence is still occurring and in the other we already have all the evidence.

This last distinction perhaps brings out the fact that although the processes of acquiring the necessary hypotheses (this is clearly an inductive process) may vary from circumstance to circumstance, the methods used remain essentially the same. We now see that this is the basic problem of induction or what when symbolized has some-times been called inductive logic. This means in turn that we must have all the available deterministic, probabilistic or statistical types of model at our disposal to make up an ideal problem-solver. We are arguing that the human being must have some of these models available in the form of existing standard techniques, which can be acquired from existing documented knowledge such as books, etc., which allow him to apply standard "corporately derived techniques" in order to solve inductive problems. This implies the distinction between knowledge by description and knowledge by acquaintance.

Problems which are initially inductive are still problems when they are reduced to the deductive form. But now the nature of the problem has changed. The inductive generalizations are now assumed to be already available; the task is really one of *recognition*. The task is to recognize which inductive generalizations are appropriate to the solution of the problem. Another problem may arise also because, although the appropriate generalizations are given or recognized, it may still not be obvious how they should be *applied*. The next stage in our argument is to show how these various types of problem arise in isolation, and then show how they are likely to be combined together in the more realistic "emotional context" of actual human behaviour.

We shall start with a discussion of a stimulus-response approach to the problem and then move to the more general question of concept-formation.

Classical conditioning experiments show circumstances where a cat, rat or dog responds discriminatingly to environmental stimuli. A Thorndike[1] cat will learn by a series of stimulus-response activities to escape from a cage. It is motivated to do so: being captive is a state which seems always to motivate an attempt to escape. There is a sense in which the act of pulling a lever, say, which releases the animal is a specific response, even though in physiological terms it may represent a whole series of responses.

A question now arises as to whether the cat has formed a concept, especially when repeatedly placed in the same situation and where escape becomes immediate. The answer would seem to be 'yes' and it has also formulated a sort of hypothesis; certainly when we think of these processes as applying to human problem solving we shall say 'yes', since we shall mean by the word 'concept' precisely the identification of individuals, classes, and relations in the environment which, as human beings, we describe, albeit vaguely, in terms of names. We can of course, talk of *connotation* and *denotation* in this human context, and as a result the context can be made more precise. We now have to be careful to identify concepts as functions of properties and classes. The concept *dog* is the conjunction of properties such as *four-legged*, *tailed*, *two-eyed*, etc. There is something about a dog which makes it different from a cat and we can, if we are careful, identify and enumerate these differences. We can also run into borderline cases between concepts (or classes), and these can usually be resolved by finer distinctions which can be made *as and when the context demands*. Classes are, in other words, often vaguely defined and "shadowy".[2]

3 Some Formalism

We shall use now some limited formalism which we shall build up in stages as we need it. We shall[3,4] say that *individuals* are denoted by

[1] E. L. Thorndike, *Animal Intelligence*, New York: Macmillan, 1911.

[2] S. Korner, Ostensive Predicates, *Mind*, 1951, *9*, 60, 80–9.

[3] R. B. Banerji, A language for the description of concepts, *General Systems*, 1964, *9*, 135.

[4] F. H. George, Hypothesis confirmation on a digital computer, *Conference on Bionics*, 1966, Dayton, Ohio.

$$\alpha, \beta, \ldots, \gamma$$

or by the use of suffices with class names as below. *Properties* by

$$x, y, \ldots, w$$

with subscripts as needed, and classes *denoted* by

$$a, b, \ldots, n$$

also with subscripts as needed. The usual connectives are to be used: . for *and* or conjunction. We use v for *or* or *disjunction*, as in *Principia Mathematica* language which entail all the usual logical connectives. Then for a concept (we shall use class name symbols primed) which is given a class name, we get

$$a \quad a.b., \ldots, c \text{ v } d \text{ v}, \ldots$$

although, of course, those features usually regarded as being necessary to a concept or class definition are the conjoined classes or properties as we now think of them. We can also deal with disjunctive classes and associated concepts.[1] So every property is itself a class, and every class of objects (individuals) is a set of properties.

We could, as we see above, drop the distinction between class and property, or diminish it to nothing, but sometimes we want to talk of an object having a property, as apart from being a member of a class, thus it seems wise to preserve both ways of talking; the context should make the distinctions that are needed.

We should also note that in talking of concepts:

$$a', b', \ldots, n'$$

we are asserting that all concepts are classes, but that not all classes are concepts. We at least reserve the right to consider classes independent of concepts whether or not we wish actually to insist on such a distinction.

These classes or properties are related to each other in a variety of ways by Operators:

$$., \text{ v}, \sim, \supset, \equiv, \ldots, \text{ etc.}$$

where the symbols stand for connectives such as conjunction, disjunction, negation, material implication, equivalence and for verbs such as 'is', 'runs' and relational phrases, such as 'to the right of', 'over', 'is a brother of', etc. Statements so derived include *hypotheses*, where they assert testable empirical propositions, usually

[1] E. B. Hunt and C. I. Hovland, Programming a model of human concept formulation, 1961, *Proc. Western Joint Computer Conf.*, 145–55.

although not necessarily, to be thought of as generalized. We shall argue that all these apparently different interpretations of the connectives are in reality the same, or sufficiently similar to allow of a common description. So we now have acceptable linguistic canonical forms:

Axa		xAa
Byb		yBb
Cab	or	aCb
Dcd		cDd
Exy		xEy

etc, which represents individual-class relationships which, when attached to an operator, allow of an empirical description, and where we are using the capital letters

$$A, B, \ldots, N$$

to stand for the connectives.

We are now in process of formulating a precise descriptive language which maps a rigorous model in symbolic form on to certain aspects of human experience. This includes that which is immediately given (appearances) and also that which is already acquired (hypothetical) and may be in generalized form. We are trying to provide a formal model of the central cognitive process. The need for such a formalism arises, of course, from our demand that our model be computable. We are clearly now thinking of problem solving within the symbolized world[1, 2] and would argue that symbolized problem solving is more general than, and includes, the non-symbolized form. The most obvious example of non-symbolized problem solving is the learning stage of a maze-running problem, although even for the sub-human organism, we cannot be certain that symbolization in some form does not occur.

4 Problems to solve

Obviously, problem solving may involve more than language alone, and the ostensive process is the means of acquiring most basic knowledge in infancy. Subsequently, knowledge is derived from both

[1] E. R. Hilgard, *Theories of Learning* (second edition), London: Methuen, 1958.
[2] E. B. Hunt, *Concept learning: an information processing problem*, New York: Wiley, 1962.

C

acquaintance and *description*. Let us next look at some particular problems. Here is a typical list of problems:[1]

1 How do we travel from Iver to Bristol in the least time, on a Friday afternoon?

2 How can we best explain Compiler languages, such as ALGOL, to someone who has never heard of them?

3 On what principles do we base our tactical and strategic play for a game such as football or contract bridge?

4 How do we, as burglars, get to know the combination lock on some safe and retrieve the contents of the safe by tomorrow?

5 How do we solve algebraic equations of the form $ax^2 + bx + c = 0$

Immediately we see that realistic problems can take various forms and their solutions require various approaches; they can have, for example, optimization 'solutions' with or without complete information. They can be problems of definition, extended here under the name 'explanation'. They can involve inductive generalizations, deductions, heuristics or algorithms. They do not, however, necessarily require what Newell, Shaw and Simon[2] called *creative* problem solving, which we will be briefly discussing later. We must also note that one common feature exists: *a problem is a situation for which a response (or set of responses) is required and that response (or set of responses) has not already been acquired, or known to be acquired.*

In a sense, therefore, problem solving is a sort of recognition and discrimination, a perception of similarities among differences and differences among similarities. We shall bear this point in mind in the next chapter.

We must now recognize that a human problem solver has, through the medium of language, the possibility of using knowledge which has been acquired not by himself (alone) but by the community in which he lives, so that a problem may be recognized as fitting into a standard technique of, say, logic, statistics, or mathematics.

To formulate hypotheses requires the use of concepts.[3,4] We

[1] F. H. George, Cognitive Models of Behaviour, To be published in a book in memory of Norbert Wiener, 1969. (In press)

[2] A. Newell, J. C. Shaw and H. Simon, Elements of a theory of human problem solving. *Psychol. Rev.*, 1958, *65*, 1951–66.

[3] F. H. George, Hypothesis confirmation on a digital computer, *Conference on Bionics*, 1966, Dayton, Ohio.

[4] F. H. George, Formation and analysis of concepts and hypotheses on a digital computer. *J. Math. Biosciences*, 1968. (In press)

may have much data in store which has not been named; this is the same as the situation of human beings who recognize a certain circumstance as frequently occurring and for which no name has been derived. We could now name such situations as needed, but in general we shall not wish to name every circumstance individually. We in fact do so only when they occur with a high degree of frequency; and where the circumstances are more or less the same on each occurrence. Also, in a similar vein, not every shape has a name; triangles, circles and regular polygons sometimes have, but there is an infinity of shapes which have not. In other words language is incomplete in vocabulary, and is like a sketchy map of territory, bringing out some features more prominently than others. The formulation of new hypotheses requires either the sorting of existing concepts (with their class names) or the creation of new concepts and the manufacture of new class names.

The biggest problem in any empirical model of logical and intelligent processes, is that of relevancy. What is relevant to a problem? The general answer (to the symbolized problem) is that if the problem (statement or question) contains *terms*, individual variables or names of individuals such as in the set

$$x \equiv x_1, x_2, x_3, x_4, a_1, a_2, a_3, a_4$$

then a *directly relevant* possibility will contain any subset of this set x. In others words, a statement directly relevant to x will contain at least one of the terms defining x.

We will expect relevant statements such as

$$A_1x_1a_5 \qquad \qquad \ldots (1)$$
$$A_2x_5a_5 \qquad \qquad \ldots (2)$$

then although (2) contains no element of the set x, it has a link with x through (1). A simple example will suffice

> "Bill is Jack's brother."
> "Jack is Irish."

and since 'brother' implies at least the following rules (its intension or *connotation* (these concepts are synonymous), or something like it):

> 1 Bill and Jack have the same parents
> 2 Bill and Jack have the same nationality
> (where 'nationality' must be defined) we can infer
> "Bill is Irish."

Thus if we know that an Irishman is the local postman, it could be Bill, just as well as Jack.

The whole problem of relevancy depends upon building up a logical chain of arguments wherein it is possible to follow through from premises to conclusion, whether these be causal or analytic. This is always implicit in human arguments, although not always made explicit. It is often easy for the human being to accept "jumps" in a logical chain, since the intermediate steps, making up the jumps, are so familiar and so standard as not to need taking. This implicitness must be made explicit in the computer program.

5 Explanation

We must, when theorizing about human thinking, also consider related topics such as scientific explanation and induction, or inductive logic. These subjects indeed form a major part of this book. We can at this stage say that an explanation of an event, or events, is a description, where we mean the description to apply to the causal chain of events leading to the event needing explanation. This can be made a matter of any degree of depth whatever. We must provide some formalization of the process and at this stage will simply refer to the use of reduction sentences, and their use in the field of "scientific" explanation. An explanation of some events or events can take the form of reduction sentences, or other explanatory statements. Carnap[1] has suggested the form

$$A(x) [P(x) \supset Q(x) \equiv R(x)]$$

where x is, in the example say, a substance soluble in water, R is the concept to be explained and satisfies the conditions for x if, and only if, when it (x) is immersed in water (P), it dissolves (Q).

The main point about this technique of explanation is that it tells you what would have happened *if* you had done something, even though you do not actually do it. This is one form of empirical description which is explanatory, and in similar form can be used to analyze degrees of confirmation, degrees of factual support, etc., of scientific theories. The point to note here is that this apparently takes us beyond problem solving to the *justification* of the solutions to

[1] R. Carnap, Testability and Meaning. *Phil. Sci.*, 1937, *3*, 419–71; *4*, 1–40.

problems. The reason for its relevance is that in simulation we can sometimes only know solutions to be solutions by virtue of accumulating subsequent evidence. This is one aspect of the distinction between the generating of solutions (discovery) and the verifying of processes (justification). When we try to describe an effective process to achieve the same ends, we cannot now so easily maintain this distinction. It is also clear that definitions, as well as explanations, are part of the equipment which is needed to clarify, explain or solve a problem, in the sense of our specific examples.

Let us now return to thinking, or symbolized problem solving, which is a vital part of thinking. Our approach now goes back to the very general, and deals with the basic definition and the beginnings of the problem.

We should emphasise again before concluding this chapter that we are thinking primarily in hypothetico-deductive terms. Explanations can take many forms and go into any degree of detail, but they are to be thought of as being embedded in a background which formulates and tests hypotheses and reorganizes those hypotheses as necessary.

The treatment of methodological matters in this chapter claims no more precision than seems necessary to justify what follows, especially in Part II.

3

Perception

1 Perception, Recognition and Recall

By 'perception' we mean the process of interpreting stimuli in the environment. This involves *classification* of novel stimuli or novel combinations of stimuli, and the *recognition* of familiar stimuli, or sets of stimuli, where the interpretation of the input is now clearly connected with the process of *recall*.

The assumption is that we cannot perceive or recognize other than by some form of comparison between the input and what has previously been stored. In other words no perception, and as a result no intelligent behaviour, can occur in any automaton which is not able to store information from the past. This is not to say that the innate structures of the organic systems do not play a significant part in the actual process of perceiving (Gestalt Theory), but whilst this structural consideration is a relevant factor, the more significant factor is the *method* of perceiving which must lie in a comparison between the present and the past.

The basic method suggested by Hayek[1] and Uttley[2] is that of classification. If one could label all the "primitive stimuli", or sense data, that the human being is subject to, it could then be argued that every physical object and every sensory occurrence can certainly be built up by classification. We can expect to build a system indeed which could recognize anything whatever; the logical argument for a *complete* classification system being capable of complete recognition seems unanswerable.

Unfortunately, as far as simulation is concerned, difficulties spring

[1] S. A. Hayek, *The Sensory Order*, Chicago: University of Chicago Press, 1952.
[2] A. M. Uttley, The classification of signals in the nervous system. *EEG Clin. Neurophysiol.*, 1954.

from the fact that the number of neurons which would appear to be needed for such a recognition model is astronomical and far in excess of the number available in any human nervous system.

The answer to this problem of dimensions could lie in a misunderstanding as to the way in which the human classification system is constructed. It is possible that a neuron does not play a single role in a one single neural network, but may be capable of playing a part in various different networks as a result of different states of the nervous system prevailing at any particular time. But on the whole this suggestion seems less probable than the alternative one which is that classification in the nervous system cannot be complete, but must be partitioned, partial and adaptive. By *partitioned* we mean the system must be built up in modalities as in a family tree (obviously initially separate for each sensory modality); by *partial* we mean simply incomplete and by *adaptive* we mean subject to change as a function of changing circumstances.

In describing models of perception, we should emphasize that this chapter is in no sense an attempt to survey the field. We should, however, mention two types of model called "genotypic" and "monotypic".[1] In a genotypic model it is supposed that the detail of the structure of the recognition model is not to be specified with full anatomical detail. Instead, mathematical and statistical operators are used to specify the function, rather than make any attempt to complete detailed structures. The monotypic system, on the other hand, supplies detail with as much structural precision as is needed. The networks of Uttley[2] are an example of a monotypic system. As has been pointed out elsewhere[3] there is another consideration which cuts across the difference between a monotypic and a genotypic system and that is whether a model is "special purpose" or "general purpose". Arguments have been advanced in favour of specific special purpose receptor systems[4] whereas other arguments have been put in favour of general purpose principles.[5]

At this stage the sort of judgment that seems called for is one that says that a monotypic system is desirable as long as it is feasible, and

1 F. Rosenblatt, *Principles of Neurodynamics*, Spartan Books, 1962.

2 A. M. Uttley, The conditional probability of signals in the nervous system. RRE Memo. No. 1109, 1955.

3 F. H. George, *Cybernitcs and Biology*, Edinburgh: Oliver & Boyd, 1965.

4 J. Drever, Perceptual learning, *Ann. Rev. Psychol.*, 1960, *11*, 131–60.

5 W. M. O'Neil, Basic issues in perceptual theory, *Psychol. Rev.*, 1958, *65*, 348–61.

a genotypic system is acceptable when a monotypic system has ceased to be feasible. There is indeed no exclusive distinction between these two types of modelling procedure; a final consideration is the purpose of the enquiry and the context.

As far as the labels 'special purpose' and 'general purpose' are concerned it seems again that both are possible and although the human visual system, for example, seems to have specialized receptors with certain inevitably specialized characteristics—and this is one of the points that the Gestalt theorists were making—in the form of eyes (ears and the sensory endings of touch and taste etc., are also relevant to the full sensory range), the principles on which this information is processed more centrally seems capable of being stated in general terms. Thus, it seems likely that the sort of distinctions that have been made in the past about such models are not as important as they may have seemed at the time. We shall, at any rate in this Chapter try to discover general principles since, although we recognize the existence of special purpose sensory equipment, we shall suppose that it supplies information which is capable of being processed in a general way.

This is much like saying that if you have digitizers in a system it does not matter by what sort of equipment the sensory information is acquired, but that when collected it is all processed in a similar manner. This last statement may be taken as supporting the general perceptual theorist against the special purpose theorist, and in some part this is true. But it is true only in part since it is still recognized that special purpose sensory equipment exists.

2 Pattern Recognition in Perception

Our basic problem is that of *pattern-recognition* and, although this occurs at all levels, including the conceptual levels of human behaviour, we are considering it here in the narrow context of visual pattern recognition. We are suggesting that the basic method by which this is possible, is one of classification of information where that classification does not primarily take place at the actual retinal level. The classification is partial and hierarchical and takes place at the first stage, second stage, and perhaps at a third and fourth stage in the visual cortex. Complete classification must be replaced by adaptive classification, although it looks as if an argument can be made out for saying that the maximum flexibility occurs in the early years of the life of the organism and as time goes by the classifying system loses a great deal of its adaptivity. This is plausible on purely logical grounds, of course, since as you fill up all the vacant spaces in a filing system or any other sort of classification system so the number of spaces for new information diminishes. This implies, probably correctly, that the human nervous system finds it more difficult to reorganize combinations of stimuli than it does to organize them in the first instance.

It might be asked at this stage what merit there is in what we might call partial self-classification. The answer is that whereas a complete classification caters for every conceivable possibility, the vast bulk of possibilities which could be recorded but never occur are not used; a partial classification system classifies only those events which actually occur, say in the visual field. We can think in terms of the visual modality, even though the argument seems to be perfectly general. This means that every possible set of properties, i.e. every event or physical object, is either recognized by comparison with an existing record, or classified as "new" and put into an existing but general, classification. Alternatively, a new classification may be set up as a result of the properties it possesses. No doubt such classifications are complicated and "cross associative" but we shall not discuss that there. 'New', above, in any case must be always related to what is already known.

It is classification with possible reorganization in the light of further experience that we call self-classifying, and this is really a form of adaptation. If the picture at this stage seems too symmetrical and too well organized, let us say that we are concerned here with simulating brainlike methods. This means starting with idealized models. Models with standard sets of artificial neurons working in a highly systematic and symmetrical way can be built. In practice, human beings have sets of neurons which vary enormously in their sensitivity and in other properties, and operate in part by chemical as well as by physical stimulation and transmission of stimuli, even, though they do so on rather generalized principles of combination which are subject to a considerable amount of error.

From what has been said above, it seems likely that the actual neural classification system available in a human being, is a rougher, cruder approximation to the sort of abstract conceptual model we have in mind at this moment. All this we accept as a necessary part of the evolution of any simulation model.

One further point about the perceptual model we are presupposing is that the partial self-classifying system takes place in a series of stages, involving special purpose receptors, the transmission taking place through partial hierarchical classification to the cortical centres. At the same time information is passed to other control centres in the brain, and this is followed by further visual classification, followed in turn by further (possibly many) stages of conceptual classification and re-classification.

If perception is thought of as the process of classifying and possibly re-classifying, and recognition is thought of as comparing an existing input with a previously stored input (which in practice will certainly involve an "attempt" on the part of human beings to remember the name of the object or objects) then the process of recall is involved in this latter stage. This is not to say, of course, that recall is concerned only with the remembering of names of physical objects; it is not. One can be told a name and asked to recall the face, as distinct from recognizing the face when shown a set of photographs and asked to say who the person is. So recall can involve the complex matter of *imagery*.

We are primarily concerned with thinking but we must admit the importance of imagery; this presents a very complicated and difficult problem, and in this chapter we shall be concerned with indicating only our general attitude to imagery. We shall say that one of the properties of the human nervous system is to be able to recall things from storage, which has an effect similar to that of the stimulation which took place at original perception or at stages of recognition, and this has some of the "conscious feelings" associated with the original stimulation. This is perhaps because some, usually small, percentage of the original input fibres are reactivated and one has almost a reconstructed picture of events from the past. It is well known that people cannot actually *see* the details of a building or a face again, but have the feeling that they "almost" can. We feel that this is the basic feature which underlines the process of imagery, and is essential to the process often called imagination.

3 Perceptual Learning

If there is any one chink in the armour of the argument that perception is a purely interpretive and receptive system, that chink is embodied in the words "perceptual learning".

Drever[1] in a particularly clear exposition on the subject of perceptual learning, starts by saying:

'In psychology our subject matter keeps confounding our distinctions, and what we have set apart we must always bring together again. So it is with perception and learning.'

We have already emphasised the overlap of meaning of the terms used in describing cognitive functions, and this overlap is emphasised if the problem of perception and learning, and their relationship, is reduced to that of trying to fit perception into a Hullian type of theory; this would seem to be an essentially unwise procedure. But before suggesting anything more constructive, let us look further at the sort of distinction made by Drever, and O'Neil[2] before him.

O'Neil suggested a three-way classification of perceptual theories:

1 Discrimination Theories (e.g. Skinner, Gibson).

2 Phenomenalist Theories (e.g. Gestalt, Michotte, Gibson).

3 Judgmental Theories (e.g. Woodworth, Bartley, Vernon and the Transactionalists).

It will be noted that Gibson has been placed in two groups, and this situation is eased by Drever's four-way classification where the four groups are:

1 Judgmental Theories (as in O'Neil).

2 Stimulation Theories (Gestalt theories and Michotte).

3 Association Theories (Gibson).

4 Adaptation Theories (Köhler's later work, Hochberg, etc.).

The emphasis on learning-in-perception places Gibson wholly in the Associationist group, while the new group is concerned with showing that perceptual phenomena, as in the case of prismatic lens adaptation,[3] can be adaptive.

We accept that all perceptual theories could and should include the adaptive factors, which are well documented in terms of such experimental work as the figural after-effects and movement after-effects.[4,5] We accept that perceptual mechanisms must indeed be classificatory, and we see 'identification', 'interpretation' and

1 J. Drever, Perceptual learning, *Ann. Rev. Psychol.*, 1960, *11*, 131–60.

2 W. M. O'Neil, Basic issues in perceptual theory, *Psychol. Rev.*, 1958, *65*, 348–61.

3 I. Köhler, *Überautbau und wandlungen der wahrenhomongsweldt*, Rohrer, Vienna, 1951.

4 F. H. George, On the figural after-effect, *Quart. J. Exp. Psychol.*, 1953.

5 F. H. George, On the theory of the figural after-effect, *Canad. J. Psychol.*, 1953, *7*, 167–71.

'classification'[1,2] as characteristic of such classificatory methods. We want somehow to give due weight also to associationism and the nature of the stimulus itself. There are two paramount considerations that we must bear in mind:

1 Perception is not merely passive acceptance of input stimuli. It is a complex interactive process, closely related to memory and therefore often closely related to thinking as has been recognized most clearly by the Judgmental Theorists.

2 A related point to the first one is that vagueness in the words we use[3] confuse the perceptual picture in so many ways, above all by use of the word 'perception' itself.

Our hope is that our models will clarify these problems, and we remain aware that there is the possibility of naivety in that the subtler points of distinction between different perceptual theories may be overlooked. This we must be aware of, and accept that first order approximations are inevitable. We shall especially bear in mind the criticism made by Dreyfus[4] of the development of artificial intelligence.[5]

Briefly we shall assert that perception is a complex process and can be thought of narrowly as concerned with input identification and classification. It can be thought of, in complex terms, as closely related to thinking, problem-solving and decision taking. The only difference between the two views is one of emphasis and of semantics, and is concerned with an argument as to how complex the perceptual operation is, and how closely connected with an actual problem solving situation.

At this point we shall bring this chapter to an end in the full awareness that we have, by intention, simply drawn attention to what seems the most important features of perception in its relation to thinking.

---

[1] A. T. Welford, *Ageing and Human Skill*, London: Oxford University Press, 1958.

[2] S. H. Bartley, *Principles of Perception*, New York: Harper, 1958.

[3] F. H. George, *Cognition*, London: Methuen, 1962.

[4] H. L. Dreyfus, *Alchemy and Artificial Intelligence*, Rand Memo, p. 3244, 1965.

[5] F. H. George, The current state of artificial intelligence, a paper read at the N.A.T.O. conference on Artificial Intelligence, Paris, 1967.

Thinking

1 Thinking as Emergent from Learning

Thinking is assumed to emerge from other simpler cognitive processes, and from problem-solving and language in particular. We shall try to integrate the writing of the past with that of the present by suggesting that data-processing, especially where it involves human sources of information, although to a less extent even where it does not, will involve the use of what we would call the storing of *models* of the sources of information. Such models have in the past been called *schemas*,[1,2] and we shall return later to the closeness of the concept of a schema to the present need for internal models.

If we think of a computer as processing data in a combined on-line and off-line manner, and this is our analogy with human thinking, we must think of information as coming from particular sources. A long range radar net will pick up information from various sources and test it for consistency and could retain some adjustable measure of the level of reliability of each independent information source. If it hopes to learn from experience it must proceed in precisely this manner to accumulate information, which, among other things, tells it which information source is likely to be most reliable.

We shall argue now that schemata can be said to integrate information into a coherent whole. They may refer to such diverse features of human behaviour as the body-position, or the attitude taken to some subject matter such as classical music, or to the reliability of an individual information source. It is therefore possible to translate

---

[1] Sir H. Head, *Aphasia and kindred disorders of speech*, London: 1920.
[2] Sir F. C. Bartlett, *Thinking*, London: Allen and Unwin, 1958.

from our use of the word 'model' directly into the use of the word 'schema' and mean much the same thing.

2 Philosophers, Psychologists and Thinking

Many experiments have been carried out on human beings that have been reported under the word 'thinking' and this has been largely the work of psychologists, the more recent of which we shall look at later. Philosophers in talking of thinking sometimes regard the word as being appropriate to part at least of what we are 'consciously aware' and that only. Not that all of which we are consciously aware is thinking, but all thinking is something of which we are consciously aware. Clearly this usage is a matter of semantics, and it would seem better to take a rather broader view of thinking, as a process involving internal organic modification, yet accompanied by symbolization. That much of this is conscious is not doubted, but that some may also be unconscious is being asserted.

Problem-solving by symbolizing is a part of what thinking entails. Price[1] has referred to thinking as "cognition of the absent" and this draws attention to the fact that "thinking" is a word that signified for him the process accompanied by images of which we are conscious and which are not *necessarily* tied (or directly tied) to perception. We shall think of thinking as being cognizant of both the absent and the present.

The word 'thinking' is one, as we have said, that is clearly difficult to define and also overlaps other cognitive terms. We must therefore reach some sort of agreement as to what we shall mean by 'thinking'.

In Price's terms, distinctions are made between different types of thinking. *Sign-thinking*, for him, is tied to sensation, whether the sensation is external to the body or internal to it.

Although sign-thinking is tied, some thinking is free and consists of awareness of, or operations with respect to, the absent; you can "think about" drinking beer in an English pub even when in Abyssinia; this is, of course, cognizance of the absent.

The difference between tied and free thinking is one of degree and we accept the fact that here-and-now stimulation will often be a part of the thinking process and guide it even when the *object* of the thoughts is remote both in space and time.

[1] H. H. Price, *Thinking and Experience*, London: Hutchinson, 1953.

Images and language are closely connected with human thinking, and although much of thinking can be expressed in terms of logical notions such as *not*, *or*, *if*, etc, Price has argued that these *concepts* occur even at the pre-linguistic level. In fact, since language only attempts to symbolize and communicate what is already in the process of pre-linguistic development we might expect this to be the case. To put the matter more strongly, this is implicit in the whole approach of artificial intelligence.

Images, we understand subjectively. That is, we know what we mean when we refer to having an image of a person we know, or a building, etc. We must try to give some account of images, as well as language; naturally language and logic must occupy a major place in our research. Our problem is how to put all these pieces of the jigsaw together and make it scientifically handleable, i.e. testable.

Ryle[1] reminds us that in ordinary language phrases such as "he was thinking what he was doing" suggest that 'thinking' is sometimes used to suggest careful consideration of certain propositions followed by sensible action which follows from the sensible proposition. It seems though that the action could equally well be stupid even though it may not seem so at the time to the person concerned.

Thinking is "talking to oneself" as Ryle puts it. Ryle[2] points out quite rightly that the word 'thinking' is essentially vague, and can sometimes mean believing, sometimes conceiving, and so on and so forth. We accept the closeness of the relation between thinking and language, but suggest that although we may, as human beings, actually think in terms of words, we do not do so from necessity—i.e. there is such a thing as pre-linguistic thought.

3 Psychological Approaches to Thinking

We will now turn to the work of psychologists in the field of thinking. Bartlett[3] has defined 'thinking' as follows:

'Thinking is the extension of evidence in accord with that evidence; and this is done by moving through a succession of interconnected steps which may be stated at the time or left until later to be stated.'

This could be a statement of induction, and in any case is very

1, 2 G. Ryle, *The Concept of Mind*, London: Hutchinson, 1949.
3 Sir F. C. Bartlett, *Thinking*, London: Allen & Unwin, 1958.

reminiscent of Reichenbach's distinction between the context of discovery (inductive jumps) and the context of justification (the logical justification that comes later).

Bartlett's emphasis is on thinking as a skill, and he would accept that he is not searching for a universal definition in any sense; the word 'evidence', however, requires further definition.

The present author once said of thinking:[1]

'Thinking is in no essential way different from learning—although the emphasis here is on language—and consists in the formation of linguistic hypotheses from the conditional probabilities in storage that are themselves derived logically from storage, or directly transferred from the first storage system.'

This is also a limited definition and refers specifically to a hierarchical cybernetic type of learning model.[2] It omits mention of images, or consciousness, which may in that context be forgivable.

'A Dictionary of Psychology'[3] defines 'thinking' as follows:

'Any course or train of ideas, in the narrower and stricter sense, is a course of ideas initiated by a problem.'

Thinking, as we see, is not only closely related to learning, it is also closely related to problem-solving. Problem-solving is very much a part of learning and also occurs most often, in human beings, with thinking. To this extent a whole mass of experiments come within the purview of our subject, including everything from classical conditioning[4] to instrumental conditioning[5] and Ruger's puzzles[6] wherein the human subject has to disentangle bits of wire that are intertwined. Any scientist, mathematician or logician, in solving a problem is trying to gather evidence (relevant information) together to provide a solution, and the gatherer of the relevant evidence is doing what is very near to what we normally refer to as 'thinking'.

[1] F. H. George, The Brain as a Computer, Oxford: Pergamon Press, 1961.
[2] A. M. Uttley, The conditional probability of signals in the nervous system. RRE Memo, No. 1109, 1955.
[3] J. Drever, A Dictionary of Psychology, Hamondsworth: Penguin Books, 1952.
[4] I. P. Pavlov, Conditioned Reflexes, London: Oxford University Press, 1927.
[5] E. R. Hilgard and D. G. Marquis, Conditioning and Learning, London: Methuen, 1938.
[6] H. A. Ruger, The psychology of efficiency; and experimental study of the processes involved in the solutions of mechanical puzzles and in the acquisition of skill in their manipulation. Arch. Psychol., 1910, New York, 2, 15.

Another point of view, as exemplified by Wertheimer[1] and Köhler,[2] is that of the dual-process, where there is an emphasis on "seeing through the problem". This really refers to the fact that insight is taking place and leaves us to say what we mean by 'insight'. There is some obvious relevance in the notion of the "restructuring of a problem" or the "becoming aware" of new relations, something which is so often emphasised by Gestaltists and neo-Gestaltists.

Bruner, Goodnow and Austin[3] have carried out a number of experiments on thinking in which they regarded thinking as categorizing behaviour. Categorization here means much the same as classification, with special emphasis on the process of placing events, items, etc, together as a means of simplifying the environment. This is done on the basis of "sufficient similarity" for some purpose and in some context. Categorization, as they point out, has certain special advantages:

1 It reduces the complexity of the environment.
2 It is a means of identification.
3 It reduces the need for learning.
4 It is a means for action.
5 It permits the ordering and relating of classes of events.

All these features of thinking are important and they are amply illustrated by a whole series of their experiments which reveal what they call "strategies in concept attainment". Their description is extremely similar to what Newell, Shaw and Simon, and the author have called *heuristics*, and what Miller, Galanter and Pribram[4] have called *plans*.

The basis of the Bruner, Goodnow and Austin distinction is the usual one between conception and perception. Perception and conception are recognized as being closely allied but the fact is that we usually invent categories and do not discover them. This draws attention to the conventional nature of labelling or naming, even though labels may have long standing traditional backgrounds.

Finally, we must again emphasise that concept attainment is not quite the same as concept formation in that it is capable of being predicated of the absent as well as the present; this is now familiar

---

1 M. Wertheimer, *Productive thinking*, New York: Harper, 1945.

2 W. Köhler, *The Mentality of Apes*, London: Routledge and Kegan Paul, 1925.

3 J. S. Bruner, J. J. Goodnow and G. A. Austin, *A Study of Thinking*, New York: Wiley, 1956.

4 G. A. Miller, E. Galanter and K. H. Pribram, *Plans and the Structure of Behaviour*, New York: Holt, 1961.

D

ground. Clearly concepts are generalizations in some sense and are tested by virtue of their exemplars or instances of attributes—properties such as colour, weight, etc.

The attainment of a concept, as it is sometimes called, depends on distinctions or discrimination—elephants are distinguished from tigers—and there is a validatory process, which is normally "either-or", i.e. an item is either A or not-A. In fact, of course, if the either-or distinction is not made the categories become a continuum. A strategy is the set of decisions that leads to concept attainment, and can be thought of in game-theoretic terms as decisions governing a pay-off matrix.

An alternative definition of *strategy* suggested by Hunt[1] is:

'A strategy is a plan for arriving at a predestined goal at minimum cost. The goal in concept learning is the attainment of a definition of a concept which provides a satisfactory decision rule for assigning names to objects.'

Apart from the unnecessary reference to "minimum cost" the definition seems to be much the same as the first one.

Various strategies are discussed by Bruner, Goodnow and Austin and are called "conservative focusing", "focus gambling", "successive scanning" and so on. The general pattern is clear enough; one may proceed to find a satisfactory goal route through a maze by trial-and-error. One may do so by noticing only positive or successful results, by using negative instances of results, by formulating concepts or hypotheses that allow testing, and which involve either more or less risk. It is clear that one may in most test situations adopt a safe-and-slow or unsafe-and-fast technique and indeed there will generally be many other alternatives in between these limiting cases. What may act as a limiting factor is that of urgency. If you need a solution urgently then you take risks that you would not—need not—normally take.

In this context, we should mention the work of P. C. Wason,[2] who has carried out some interesting experiments on concept forma-

1 E. B. Hunt, *Concept Learning; on Information Processing Problem*, New York: Wiley, 1962.

2 P. C. Wason (with P. N. Johnson-Laird), *Thinking and Reasoning*, Hamondsworth: Penguin Modern Psychology, 1968.

P. C. Wason, The effect of self-contradiction on fallacious reasoning. *Quart. J. Exp. Psychol.*, 1964, *16*, 30–4.

P. C. Wason, On the failure to eliminate hypotheses in a conceptual task, *Quart. J. Exp. Psychol.*, 1960, *12*, 129–40.

tion. He found that most people find it more difficult to handle negative than positive information. He used diagrams as below:

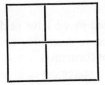

with stars, which may be coloured, in one of the quadrants. A statement which went with such a figure may be positive:

"There is a blue star in the upper right hand
quadrant."

or may be negative:

"There is no star in the lower left hand
quadrant."

He measured the errors that were made and the time taken to carry out the task, and found that true statements were handled more quickly and efficiently than false statements and that positive information was handled more quickly than negative.

A further result of Wason's was that if self-contradiction occurs and is seen to occur by a subject then fewer fallacious inferences occur as a result.

We should now repeat the point that this monograph does not aim to provide a comprehensive account of thinking or concept learning, and familiarity with much other work is assumed.

4 Concepts

A concept is defined here as a network of sign-significate inferences by which one goes beyond a set of observed criterial properties exhibited by an object or event to the class identity of the object or event in question, and thence to inferences about other unobserved properties of the object or event.

In contrast with this approach to concept formation, we have Bartlett's[1] definition of thinking which we have already quoted, but now repeat. It is based essentially on the same type of experimental problem-solving situation. This definition is:

'Thinking is the extension of evidence in accord with that evidence,

1 Sir F. C. Bartlett, *Thinking*, London: Allen & Unwin, 1958.

and this is done by moving through a succession of interconnected steps which may be stated at the time, or left until later to be stated.'

This definition is limited as we have said already, but the aspect of thinking which Bartlett is describing could easily be interpreted so as to fit the concept-formation activity described by Bruner *et al.* It is, we shall argue, a statement of induction, in that given some of the terms in say a mathematical series one may propose a general rule for the generation of the series. This may, of course, involve decisions as to its base and will be subject to validation by test.

In fact, we are assuming, following the above two views, that thinking is much the same as formulating inductive principles, which necessarily involve symbolization. This does not mean that purely deductive inferences are irrelevant but it may be assumed that the analogue of this operation in automata is relatively trivial. The main point is that the operation of categorizing is itself what we shall call an inductive operation.

Körner[1] has argued that conceptual thinking is typified, although not exhaustively illustrated, by the application and acceptance of ostensive rules. An ostensive rule is typified by a pointing operation accompanied by such a statement as "this and everything like this is green". This requires that bases for concepts be defined, and they may be defined in many ways rather as co-ordinates can be chosen in many different ways to define a space. The problem of interest that arises from Körner's work is that of the derivation of non-ostensive concepts and rules from either ostensive or non-ostensive bases.

The problems that Körner himself is most concerned with are those such as the derivation of mathematical or other such non-ostensive concepts, from ostensive or non-ostensive bases. This represents another challenge—how can, if at all, a computer program be written so as to perform these sorts of operation? It can be said straight away that this *may* turn out to involve no more than the ability to generalize, although this is a vital step and not easy to simulate over the same range as human beings operate. This is bound to remain one of the acid tests, since ultimately we must be able to simulate "original and creative" thinking, whatever that entails.

Körner himself was concerned with rules that can be applied to

1 S. Körner, *Conceptual thinking*, New York: Dover, 1959.

conceptual thinking and carefully distinguished this undertaking from the obviously empirical one of deciding how people actually use concepts. We are concerned to some extent with both problems, but primarily with the logical one of prescribing rules. An attempt will not be made in this monograph to refine the rules in the degree of detail attempted by Körner, but we may expect that his analysis will prove increasingly illuminating, when our analysis probes sufficiently deeply.

To put the matter another way, it seems reasonable to argue that this monograph represents a cross-section through philosophical, logical and psychological literature concerned with cognition, and there are obvious relations in depth and breadth with other such work, of which Körner's is a typical example.

5 Thinking, Learning and Perception

Harlow[1] has discussed the relation of thinking to learning and perception and suggests the sort of problem-solving activity subsumed under the name "thinking" should be depicted by the following four steps:

1 Perception of a situation with incentive or goal inaccessible immediately, leading to

2 Elicitation of initial alternative responses, explicit or implicit, and ranging from unlearned responses to a limited number of highly organized response tendencies, these in turn leading either to

3 Problem solution (goal attainment) or failure (withdrawal)

4 Additional reaction tendencies, which again lead to either problem solution, withdrawal, or the arousal of additional reaction tendencies.

This approach, apparently ignoring symbolization, seems more useful in describing animal activities rather than human. Although we could add easily enough the symbolizing process to what Harlow has said.

There is one last point we should mention in this brief survey of thinking. Price,[1] as we have already noted, has made the point that human beings do not always have their thinking operations closely tied to their perceptions, and this is a possible objection (perhaps

[1] H. Harlow, Thinking, In *Theoretical Foundations of Psychology*, (H. Nelson, ed.) 452–505, New York: Van Nostrord, 1951.

because of symbolization) to Harlow's argument above; the first stage of the total processing may be a function of the input system but may not be directly tied to it; indeed once the conceptual process has started one state may presumably lead to another state without further perceptual steps being involved—this means that a man may sit in silence with his eyes closed and simply "think" of one thing after another and reach a stage of thinking about something that is quite remote from his immediate surroundings at that moment.

It should also be mentioned that many of the people who have addressed themselves to the problem of thinking, have, like Körner, Price, Ryle and Wittgenstein, not been concerned with the empirical facts as such, but with supplying a logical foundation for the development of propositions, and indeed for language in general.

At the same time those who were more connected with the empirical facts, such as Bartlett, Harlow, Hunt and Hovland, among many others, have accepted the fact that language plays a vital part in human thinking.

In what way we might ask, has this brief survey of thinking helped our own search? The answer is straightforward. Different people have studied thinking, and problem-solving for different reasons and from different points of view, and much of the work of philosophers has been one stage removed from that of a rigorous simulation of cognitive activity.

Psychologists have generally been more nearly concerned with the same problem as ourselves, but have not attempted a rigorous treatment. They do however supply empirical evidence which we can use as a basis for a working model. We then need to fit empirical data into that model.

We have now come to the turning point in the text. Up to now, in Part I, we have tried to lay down a foundation for research; we have tried to clarify our use of terms and relations sufficiently for our purpose. We have also said something of our methods, and made it clear that our own approach entails all of these things as part of the process of prescribing models of a kind that are sufficiently precise to be programed on to a computer. We do not, of course, suppose that we shall have the correct prescription at this stage, but we can at least hope that our models can be shown to be self-correcting.

PART TWO

FORMAL MODELS

This second part of the monograph is meant to describe the core of an approach to thinking. Although not much computer programing detail is supplied, it is hoped that the few flow charts will help in an understanding of the approach. It is assumed that enough explanation is given to show how the various computer programs were written and how others could be written along the same lines.

The point must be made that the Chapters of Part II refer mostly to programs that have been written, tested and run on the computer, although some remain in the Systems Analysis stage. There is a certain dullness in a book that is made up largely of program print outs and flow charts, hence these have been kept to a minimum.

The aim of this section is to show how such basic features of thinking as concept and hypothesis formation, inference making and the use of ordinary English is essentially something that can be carried out by a computer.

Let us now state our basic attitude to our problem in terms of related topics.

We are thinking of stochastic learning models[1] and stimulus-sampling models[2] and Markov net models in general as providing the basic data which our information processing model has to handle.

We can think of a stochastic process as a sequence of events with

---

[1] R. Bush and F. Mosteller, *Stochastic Models for Learning*, New York: Wiley, 1955.

[2] W. K. Estes, Towards a statistical theory of learning, *Psychol. Rev.*, 1950, *57*, 94–107.

a probability of occurrence associated with each event. A Markov net is a stochastic process with the additional factor of conditional probabilities governing whole sequences, e.g. A comes after B if B comes after C, etc. By stimulus sampling, we mean to imply the techniques which statisticians normally use; take a sample and assume it to be typical; take another sample to test as needed.

We are assuming that pattern recognition, as in the case of a "learning Pandemonium"[1] is a more general procedure which provides a base for concept learning which in turn provides a base for hypothesis formation.

We are assuming further that the methods to be used reflect the human methods are are a mixture of algorithms, quasi-algorithms and heuristics. By *algorithms* we mean the usual automatic procedure of solving a problem and by *heuristics* we mean the intelligent guess or "short-cut" (a hypothesis in action) and by a quasi-algorithm we mean a sort of mixture of algorithm and heuristic.

Many models aiming in the same direction as the ones provided in this monograph are referred to in passing. We should mention especially Hovland[2] Hunt and Hovland[3] Kochen[4] Amarel[5] and Banerji.[6] These all represent somewhat similar approaches to our problem, and we shall be saying a little about each of them at the appropriate time.

[1] O. Selfridge, Pandemonium, a paradigm for learning, *Proc. Sympos. on the Mechanization of thought processes*. London, H.M. Stationery Office: 1959.

[2] C. I. Hovland, A "communication analysis" of concept learning, *Psychol. Rev.*, 1952, 69, 461–72.

[3] E. B. Hunt and C. I. Hovland, Programming a model of human concept formulation, *Proc. Western Joint Computer Conf.*, 1960, 145–55.

[4] M. Kochen, Experimental study of "hypothesis formation" by computer. *Proc. London Sympos. on Information Theory*, 1960.

M. Kochen, An experimental program for the selection of "disjunctive hypotheses", *Proc. Western Joint Computers Conf.*, 1961, 571–78.

[5] S. Amarel, An approach to automatic theory formation, In *Principles of Self-Organization*, H. von Foerster and G. W. Zopf, Jr. (eds.), Oxford: Pergamon Press, 1962.

[6] R. B. Banerji, A language for the description of concepts, *General Systems*, 1964, 9, 135.

Computer programs for the generation of new concepts from old ones, *Neure Ergebrisse der Kybernetik*, K. Steinbuch and S. W. Wagner (eds.), Munich: Oldenbourg Verlag, 1964.

5

Concept and Hypothesis Formation

1 Concepts and Hypotheses

In this chapter, we are moving away from the preliminary clarificatory analysis of cognition (Part I) and will start to define our ideas more precisely.

The reason for precision is that we wish to test the theory—it is hardly, of course, a theory as yet, but rather constitutes steps towards a theory—on a digital computer. The testing procedure by the computer also sets the limit to the precision that we wish to attain. This in turn entails the use of some mathematical and logical terminology and entails a discussion of some part of what is involved in digital computing. The knowledge of computers required need be no more than elementary and is covered by most introductory books on the subject.[1]

Our purpose is not to provide revolutionary notions as to how thinking and problem-solving occur in human beings, but to put together much of what has been suggested already in a form where it could be tested *in toto*, and not just discussed *in toto* and tested piecemeal. To this end we are, from now on, shifting our ground and thinking and talking more in computer models, and much less in terms of men and animals.

This chapter is concerned with one particular, but especially important, part of the problem of artificial intelligence, and especially of thinking, the problem of *concept formation*. This in turn grades over into *hypothesis formation*, which grades into the problem of

[1] F. H. George, *A Survey of Digital Computing*, Oxford: Pergamon Press, 1968.

evidence and the *confirmation of hypotheses*. The problem of confirmation of hypotheses, and the closely related problem of induction, are considered in more detail in Chapter 7. At the same time it must be said that there is a very close relationship between forming hypotheses and the problem of making inductions, and this forms a bridge between this chapter and the next.

In general terms, we are looking at a process which involves input, central processing and output. The output insofar as it is overt is an action (something printed on paper for the computer); insofar as it is covert, it is a change of internal state (change of attitude, viewpoint, etc, which means a change in the totality of computer instructions).

The input is the signal that impinges on the computer and that must always mean that it is in the machine code of the computer, or some language for which the computer has, or can construct, a translation into machine code. Indeed the most important part of the input procedure is that of perception and recognition. This is also a part of the central processing and cannot be wholly separated from it. Perception and recognition necessarily overlap as do both with conception. Perception means, in broad terms, the categorization of inputs, where the process of recognition is that part of perception that deals with inputs that have occurred before. In a computer system (unlike a human being) the occurrence of the same input more than once is, or can be (virtually) an insurance of recognition. Perception without recognition occurs only when the input occurs for the first time.

As we have said, perception and recognition are a part of central processing since recognition, for example, must involve a comparison between input and stored information, while perception we shall think of as the receipt and interpretation of stimuli. We have discussed these problems in Part I and will not do so again here.[1] It must be said, however, that a distinction that the system must make is between linguistic and non-linguistic inputs, as well as between inputs which already have acceptable responses and those that still require suitable responses to be associated with the stimuli, and therefore require the formation of new hypotheses. We are concerned mainly with this last class of events.

It must be mentioned in passing that the very fact that we must

[1] F. H. George, *Cognition*, London: Methuen, 1962.

encode input onto tape or card, and that we are excluded from the full sensory range of human abilities is a serious limitation on the use of the computer. We must and shall bear this in mind.

Let us look now at a general flow chart which shows the process of concept and hypothesis formation in generalized terms.

We will be concluding this introductory section of the chapter by mentioning the fact that the stages of data-processing involved are in a *hierarchy*, and we shall, in the search for heuristics,[1] normally expect to eliminate whole sets of possibilities in a heuristic tree-searching manner, until an eventual choice can be made with precision by an algorithm over a relatively small number of alternatives. To this end we should expect to repeat the process represented by the flow chart (figure 1) a number of times, *where the output of the earlier operations is to identify the location or domain of operation of the next level of descripton.* It is in the reduction of a problem to manageable size that lies one of the main use of heuristics.

We must also add that publicly accepted techniques such as those of traditional statistics, classical mathematics, linear programming, etc, may be assumed to be available to the computer as needed. Ideally these methods should be accompanied by *recognition programs* that call up each relevant process. Such recognition programs will be quite necessary when such computer activities become man-independent.

2 The Logic of Discovery for Concept Formation

Banerji[2] has developed a language (BL) as being suitable for "pattern recognition". The basic idea—one we accept and wish to use—is that *concepts* are made up of the conjunction and disjunction of properties. Thus concepts may become extremely complex, and we wish to know whether concepts can be built up by logical operations on classes or properties which, of course, are publicly observable.

[1] A. Newell, J. C. Shaw and H. A. Simon, Empirical explorations with the logic theory machine: a case study in heuristics. In *Computers and Thought*, E. A. Feigenbaum and J. Feldman (eds.), New York: McGraw Hill, 1963.

[2] R. B. Banerji, An information processing program for object recognition, *General Systems*, 5, 117, 1960.

R. B. Banerji, Computer programs for the generation of new concepts from old ones, *Neuere Ergebrisse der Kybernetik*, K. Steinbuch and S. W. Wagner (eds.), Munich: Oldenbourg Verlag, 1964.

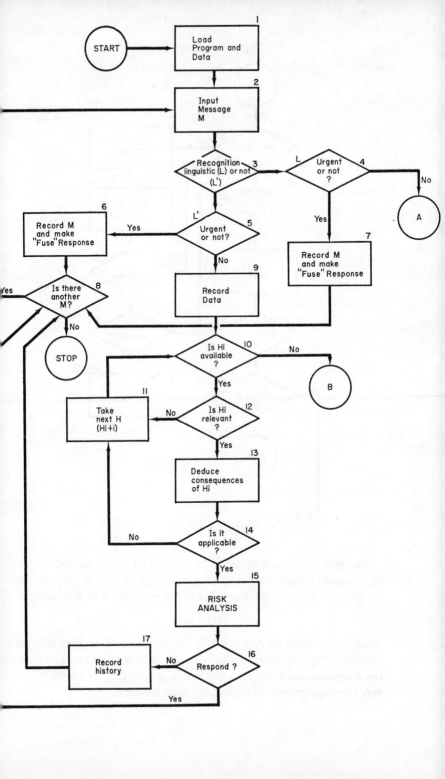

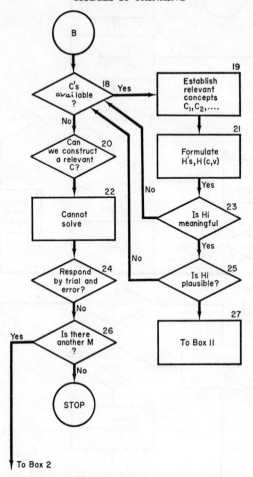

The basic operation of BL is that given an object named by the metalinguistic variable X in a metalanguage M, and a property A, we write A(X) to mean "the value of the property A in X". So:

$$A(X) = B$$

means "the value of A(X) is B". To give a concrete example, we could say "the colour of the ball is red". We use $\cap$, $\cup$ and $\rightarrow$ from the Propositional Calculus (alternative symbols to . , v and $\supset$) to carry out the process of generating such concepts.

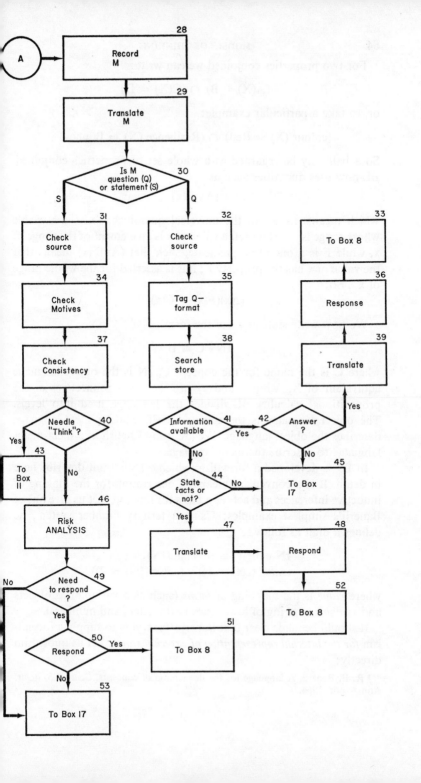

For two properties conjoined we can write:

$$(A(X) = B) \cap (C(X) = D)$$

or, to take a particular example:

$$(\text{colour } (X) = \text{Red}) \cap (\text{Resilience } (X) = \text{Bouncy})$$

So a ball may be regarded as a whole set of properties conjoined. BL now uses quantities such as

$$(Ax)F(x)$$

which means, as usual, the universal quantifier: "x is a variable whose range is a certain set, a value of x is an element of the range of x, while F is a one-place predicate, such that $(Ax)F(x)$ means that the value of x has the property F; this is asserted for the whole range of x". So:

$$(Ax)(F(x) = C(x))$$

We now write statements of the form

$$\text{IN } \epsilon \text{ C} \equiv \text{B}$$

where C is the name for the concept C, IN is the object language equivalent of X, while ϵ and $\equiv$ are the usual connectives of the propositional calculus. BL divides the language used into levels. The object language is the calculus itself, while a meta-language describes the object language. We are using English as a meta-meta-language to describe the meta-language.

In BL is developed a formalism which we shall not describe here in detail. It is a convenient means of description for the making of inductive inferences and acts as a basis for naming. Let us give one of Banerji's simplest examples: Using a ternary number system, he defines a digit as follows:

$$\text{IN } \epsilon \text{ digit} \equiv (((\textit{value } (\text{IN}) = 0) \text{ v}$$
$$(\textit{value } (\text{IN}) = 1)) \text{ v } (\textit{value } (\text{IN}) = 2))$$

where *value* is the mapping of *terms* (such as a variable) to objects and *symbols* (a string of lower case Latin letters and numbers).

It should be made clear that Banerji[1] is trying to supply a formalism *for the internal representation of external states.* Let us quote him directly:

[1] R. B. Banerji, A language for the description of concepts, *General Systems*, Ann Arbor, 1964.

'While other attempts at flexible information processing language have generally attempted facile man-machine communication in English, we have restricted ourselves to strengthening the internal representation alone: the problem of translating from English to internal representation (the semantics) has been left out as a separate problem.'

Banerji also makes the obvious point that such descriptions of concepts and languages for pattern recognition can become impossibly large.

We should say here that one of the main points of a *definition* is to reduce the enormous size of an internal description. This occurs in much the same way as in an ordinary linguistic definition, so that we can refer to a *man* in general or to Mr Smith in particular, and do not attempt to prescribe man in terms of his almost infinite number of defining properties. This re-coding procedure, or *definitions* as we call them in more familiar terms, must be used in any language to make that language economic to handle. Furthermore we do not attempt exhaustive definition, but refer to as many properties as are necessary to distinguish one class from another in a particular context, and for a particular purpose.

In this monograph we shall develop our own language for concept formation which is similar to Banerji's BL. We shall take this language to be for the internal representation, rather than the means of external communication. Then in Chapter 8 we consider the translation from this internal representation into ordinary English. This entails what Banerji calls the Semantic Rules.

We should add that a new research monograph has just appeared[1] which takes further this very complicated matter of pattern recognition and language in the context of problem solving. A consideration of this latest work is not included, but the work should be consulted by all those interested in the subject.

The BL definition given above of a digit in a ternary system is intuitively obvious, and says simply that the digit is capable of taking the value 0, 1 or 2. We shall ourselves be more concerned with the defining of (or naming of) physical objects or concepts from everyday life and less with the concepts of mathematics at this stage. We shall, however, be taking some note of concepts like *denotation* or

---

[1] R. B. Banerji, *Some Results in a Theory of Problem Solving*, Case Research Center Monograph, Parts I and II, 1968.

E

extension and *connotation* or *intension* as an understanding of these is essential to an artificially intelligent computer, since an artificially intelligent computer must have humanlike linguistic capacities. Partly because our aim is different and partly because human beings generally find it easier to follow their own nomenclature, we are going to develop a terminology which is somewhat different from that developed by Banerji.

We shall now develop our own terminology.[1] Let us repeat the basic definitions stated in Part I. Classes will be named:

$$a, b, \ldots, n$$

and properties named:

$$x, y, \ldots, w$$

and individuals named:

$$\alpha, \beta, \ldots, \omega$$

we say each class of objects such as a, say, is a set of properties, even though we also wish to be able to distinguish a class from a property.

$$\text{e.g.}: a = (x \cap y \cap z)$$

where $\cap$ is as in BL, and means conjunction.

e.g.: The class of all Welshmen = people
born in Wales *and* of Welsh parents.

But we immediately see problems; some properties are necessary to the class (i.e. they define it), others are not, and either set may be constant or variable. For example, we may say to be born in Wales is unnecessary to being Welsh, but to have Welsh parents *is* necessary. All Welsh people may speak with a Welsh accent, but this is not necessary, at most it is a contingent property.

Properties may be constant or variable; this is important. We can say that all balls are necessarily spherical, but they are not necessarily red, even though they must necessarily have a colour. Even this presents a problem since certain objects called 'balls' (e.g. rugby footballs) are not spherical, but approximately ellipsoidal. Doubts may arise therefore about the *necessary*, or defining, property of ball.

A particular ball is a constant (an individual)—for practical purposes—and has a particular size, colour, etc. A ball, in general,

[1] F. H. George, Formation and analysis of concepts and hypotheses on a digital computer, *J. Math. Biosciences*, 1968. (In press.)

is defined only as a spherical (or ellipsoidal) object, so if a is the class of all balls, and x is the property of being spherical, then

$$a = x$$

or if y is ellipsoidal then

$$a = x \cup y$$

where $\cup$ means disjunction.

If we ignore the ellipsoidal ball then x is the constant necessary defining property and all the remaining properties of colour, size, etc., while necessarily occurring, are variable. So

$$a_1 = (x \cap y_1 \cap z_1 \cap l_1 \cap m_1 \cap \ldots)$$

We shall use suffices here for particular properties which characterize an individual. So we can rewrite the above as

$$\alpha = (x \cap y \cap z \cap l \cap m \cap \ldots)$$

Suppose we say let

$$a = \text{class of all balls}$$
$$b = \text{class of all sheds}$$
$$c = \text{class of all cylinders}$$

and let the properties be defined:

$$x = \text{spherical}$$
$$y = \text{circular}$$
$$z = \text{square}$$
$$v = \text{cylindrical}$$
$$l = \text{red}$$
$$m = \text{blue}$$
$$n = \text{green}$$
$$o = \text{striped}$$
$$p = \text{yellow}$$
$$q = \text{shed}$$

and suppose we observe four particular individual objects, which are a green-and-yellow striped ball, a red ball, a blue shed, and a red cylinder. These are defined:

$$\alpha_1 = (x \cap o \cap n \cap p) \qquad \ldots (1)$$
$$\alpha_2 = (x \cap l) \qquad \ldots (2)$$
$$\beta_1 = (q \cap m \cap z) \qquad \ldots (3)$$
$$\gamma_1 = (v \cap l) \qquad \ldots (4)$$

The definition of β_1 shows the necessary characteristic q and the contingent, but general, characteristic z. We could presumably omit the necessary characteristics after use, since to say, for example, that 'a cylinder is cylindrical' is unnecessary unless we say that 'cylindrical' is shorthand for 'circular cross-section, and of straight sides, etc'. This though is relative to our definition of 'cylinder' (cf. the case of 'ball').

We must now add the definition of l_1 from above, as it appears in general form as:

$$l = (b_2 \cap c_1) \qquad \ldots (5)$$

If our universe is limited to objects (1) to (4) then (5) ostensively defines *red*. our process clearly represents a complex cross-classifying system.

Let us look now at disjunctive properties. If a cylinder can be either elliptical (j) or circular (y), but not both, we must mean (unusually) to think of 'or' as being exclusive (cf. the case of 'ball' once more).

We must remember that in Boolean Algebra 'or' is normally inclusive. Here we are using it exclusively; so if we use * for the "inclusive or" operation, then the two are related as follows:

$$a \cup b = (a * b) - (a \cap b)$$

where $-$ means 'subtraction' much as in ordinary arithmetic $\cup$ Then

$$c = (v \cap (j \cup y)) \qquad \ldots (6)$$

and since it must not be spherical, say, it could also be written:

$$c = (v \cap (j \cup y) \cap \sim x) \qquad \ldots (7)$$

although generally there is no need to add the non-existing properties to our definition.

We are finally concerned with the process of the formation of concepts and hypotheses for testing, and this certainly also involves *naming*, which is fundamental to semantic analysis and deduction. Indeed many people regard concept attainment and naming as the same procedure.

It could, of course, be argued that the process of building up *individuals* as sets of properties belonging to classes, is precisely the process of hypothesis formation. We will suggest that this is, in fact, most appropriately called concept formation and differs, but only in degree, from hypothesis formation.

Hypotheses, we shall say, are empirical statements and refer to relationships between separate (or separable) individuals or classes, whereas concepts refer to the constituents of those individuals or classes.

> *woman* is a concept
> *shed* is a concept
> "All sheds are cylindrical"
> and
> "Some women are fat"

are hypotheses or statements. All hypotheses are statements, and in a sense all indicative statements are hypotheses, but we think of hypotheses as usually being fairly general statements. So to return to our symbolism, we can write concepts in such forms as:

$$\alpha \equiv b.c.d\ldots.$$
$$\beta \equiv b\,v\,c\,v\,d\,v\ldots$$
$$\gamma \equiv b.c.d\ldots.e\,v\,f\,v\,g\,v\ldots$$

The process of concept formation on the computer is similar to that of induction, and we show a flow chart (figure 2) for a simple example such as (6) above written as in (9):

$$c \equiv v.(j\,v\,y)$$

We can regard individuals as (usually *dismemberable*) collections of properties, and we test for necessary and contingent properties with respect to any individual. We shall, in terms of computer compiled languages, name these process in two stages as:

$$CAT(n,m)$$

which categorizes an individual at level n with properties, the first of which is in address m where we are using lists of properties. Then

$$CON(n,m)$$

means form individual or concept with the necessary properties, starting at address n and with contingent properties starting at address m. This is all we shall say about the computerizing of the process at this point.

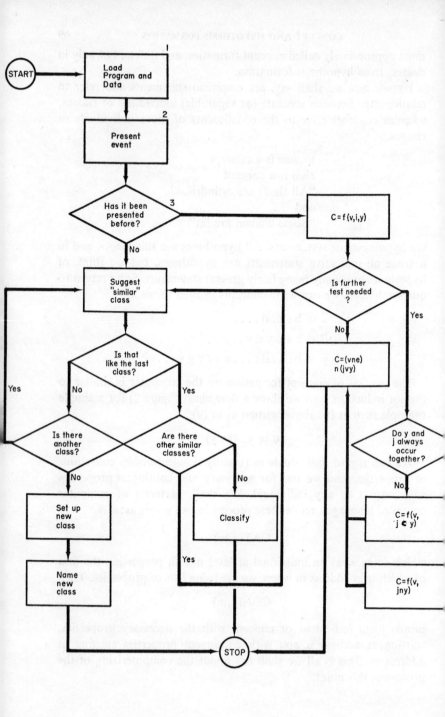

Names and Definitions

So far we have been concerned mainly with the discovery of concepts and individual examples of them; this leads naturally to the process of *naming*. We need first to be clear that *individuals* (or objects) must appear as separate integral items of the environment.

Every shed, for example, is a single separate integral item; so is every ball, every woman, and indeed everything which can be regarded as separate and whole in any obvious sense. This does not mean that a whole object cannot be dismembered, or that individuals may not coalesce and become a larger individual, but we must clearly recognize the parts from the whole in which they "normally" occur. This all refers once more, in practice, to a particular context at a particular time and for a particular purpose.

Viewed from the computer point of view, the process of naming is one of replacing a set of properties making up an individual by a single name—a class name and a member's name.

So we have the definition of an individual object α as a set of conjoined properties:

$$\alpha = a \cap b \cap c \cap d \cap e \cap f$$

We now say let α 'stand for' $a \cap b \cap c \cap d \cap e \cap f$ wherever that set appears, so that if we have:

$$a \cap b \cap c \cap d \cap e \cap f \cap (g \cup h) \cap (i \cup j) \ldots$$

then we can write this as

$$\alpha \cap (g \cup f) \cap (i \cup j) \ldots$$

α is the name of the individual or object, so α is 'man' for example, where each exemplar of α, i.e. $\alpha_1, \alpha_2, \ldots, \alpha_n$ is a particular name such as 'Bill', 'Harry', 'Charlie', etc.

In our computer terms, we may use names at any stage, but we must supply rules for their use. We tentatively suggest the following conditions:

1 When names are used by others.

2 When an individual object is 'frequently' described, where we also need some formal definition of *frequently*.

3 In order to simplify a description by substitution.

In particular uses of concept formation we can, of course, always choose suitable rules, and the rules themselves, whether particular or general, can be thought of as hypotheses and a source of learning.

In terms of a compiler language, we can use a word such as:

$$NAM(x,n)$$

where x is to be interpreted as the name for the set of properties starting at register with address n.

For our computer exploration of concepts and names we must clarify one or two further points of definition. It should be made clear that these points are *not* being proposed as a solution to a philosophical problem. We are simply defining terms in the computer programs designed to carry out our logical inference making, in the context of ordinary language. One point we shall return to again later is that we can and perhaps must have in our collections of computer programs meta-programs which will monitor, re-sort, and re-organize programs. This sort of flexibility is ultimately vital and is reminiscent of consciousness in a human being. This part of the hierarchical organization is where one level of activities is modified by a higher level. As always it is *relevancy* which is the vital key concept, and relevancy implies similarity tests such as are implied by classification.

4 Naming, Connotation and Denotation

We now suggest what is hoped to be a consistent and clear cut terminology for the use of names, one which we have tried to follow in the text so far.

We will say that a name 'X' denotes X, e.g. 'Boston' *denotes* Boston. We will say that a name 'X' *connotes* the properties of X, e.g. "Boston is a large city", "Boston is a port", etc, where the totality of true statements which are predictable of Boston, are its connotation.

In fact, when referred to a proper name like 'Boston', the use of a connotation is irrelevant, since we should not say "what does 'Boston' mean?", but if said, the answer should be " 'Boston' means nothing, but it denotes a city in Massachussetts, U.S.A."; it is a label; Boston is in fact a *concept*.

If we say "what does 'small' mean?", we say that "'small' denotes the class of anything below a certain size" (this is relative and vague), and "'small' connotes nothing other than what the word denotes".

Let us look now at a classical example such as 'The King of France'. This may denote nothing at some time t, although it has denoted something at other times and could again. If we ask "what does 'The King of France' mean?", we should say "the person who might at any time be monarch of France", or some other circumlocution which is more or less synonymous with 'The King of France'.

Denotation and *connotation* are to be thought of as more or less identical for *words*, and we should only look for a distinction between them with respect to sentences. Before moving on to statements, or their expression in sentences, we should add that the denotation of a term may be null, and all we need to know is how the *label* could be applied should the denotation be non-null. In other words we can make up what names we like and they can be labels of ideas, real or imaginary in the physical world, but their meaning occurs only in the context of a complete sentence.

From the computer viewpoint again, we can think of a label as denoting, like a name on a map, while the connotation is the set of entailments or true statements about the place. But given only the latter such a distinction becomes unimportant.

Sentences (complete statements) are meaningful we shall say if we know how, in principle, to test them for truth, whether or not the test can be actually carried out. Empirical statements are, in general, hypotheses. Logical statements are analytic and testable only for consistency.

By an *entailment*, we shall mean the connotation of a statement or of a term, e.g. "being married" entails "having a wife"or "having a husband". A term here is usually a phrase and not a single name label. By *synonymity* we shall mean terms that can be interchanged without changing the connotation (meaning) of the statement.

We have so far discussed concepts, hypotheses and touched on induction in rather general terms, while making specific reference to Banerji's work. There are however other similar approaches we should briefly examine. In examining them, we must consider differences and similarities of purpose and of treatment.

5 Amarel's Model

Saul Amarel[1] developed what he thought of as an automatic theory maker.

He took the propositional calculus as his problem solving domain and treated such problems as a testing ground for machine hypothesis making. The machine works on a heuristic basis and produces, by inductive means, routines which can be used to encourage further learning. The problem can be short circuited, in that a heuristic may be used to "guess at" an answer before the tree-searching operation is completed.

Concepts for Amarel are, as they are for us, classes or class names. What is needed is to know to what class an object belongs and something about its denotation and connotation. Hypotheses are generated in terms of the language used and problems dealt with, and these in turn produce specific information for the machine. These can be used in dealing with problems and finding their solution (e.g. theorem statement and proof, or a game and its algorithm) or dealing with associated features of the environment. Given the possibility of a range of information, such problems are posed to the machine as having to provide an accurate representation of a particular class of events. This entails, according to Amarel, the need for an information processing routine. These routines are built up from previously stored information and can be used to provide various patterns of routines (or plans) to solve new problems. Plans here are to be thought of in much the same way as in Newell, Shaw and Simon,[2] Miller, Galanter and Pribram[3] and Hunt and Hovland.[4] The problem method here is explicitly that of induction.

Two minor ways in which Amarel's work is different from the model developed in this book is in notation and type of problem

[1] S. Amarel, An approach to automatic theory formation, In *Principles of Self-organization*, H. von Foerster and G. W. Zopf, Jr. (eds.), Oxford: Pergamon Press, 1962.

[2] J. Newell, J. C. Shaw and H. A. Simon, Report on a general problem solving program, *Proc. International Conf. on Information Processing*, Paris, 1959, 250–64.

[3] G. A. Miller, E. Galanter and K. H. Pribram, *Plans and the structure of behaviour*, Holt, 1960.

[4] E. B. Hunt and C. I. Hovland, Programming a model of human concept ormulation, *Proc. Western Joint Computer Conf.*, 1960, 145–55.

domain considered. The goals are the same, but there are two other important differences:

1 There is no attempt in Amarel's system to link it with natural language, and

2 The problem of relevancy has not been considered, since he assumes all the subsets of descriptive elements with respect to any class or set are automatically relevant.

These points of difference are not of course to be read as criticisms, since Amarel's work seems to be wholly in tune with what we are trying to achieve.

6   Kochen's Model

Kochen[1] has developed an algorithmic procedure, as opposed to a heuristic one, for developing hypotheses to solve problems. He thinks of a problem situation which is defined by the need to complete some statement of class membership, say, and for this purpose presupposes the objects (represented by so-called "trit" words) and their classification have already been decided.

Kochen is concerned with a machine that can, for example, perceive a red square, a blue circle, a blue square, a green circle and a green square and on being told that they were positive or negative instances of a concept, can say what the relevent concept is. To the above set of coloured squares and circles, if the answers to the problem of relevancy has been Yes-No-Yes-No-Yes, the relevant concept would be *square*. If the answers had been No-Yes-Yes-No-No, the relevant concept would be *blue*.

This sort of operation is sometimes called *concept learning*, but the closeness of concept learning to hypothesis formation is here clear for all to see.

Although Kochen is providing an algorithm for the purpose, the inductive step of a "guess" can be made on limited evidence, as it indeed must in situations where the evidence is unlimited. This last case will arise often where the problem posed is in nature itself rather than in the form of a person asking a question.

Kochen has written most elaborate programs with complicated criteria of performance. The goals involved are more or less the same

1 M. Kochen, Experimental study of 'hypothesis formation' by computer. *Proc. London Sympos. on Information Theory*, 1960.

as with Amarel, although in the first phase the emphasis is on synthesis and not simulation.

The differences between Kochen's work and the ideas presented in this monograph are not great. However, the exclusion of natural language and the fact that a solution to any problem is known to be available among a finite set of possible solutions are two differences. Similarities exist in relation to consistency of information stored and the emergence of new hypotheses as the result of sufficient inconsistency.

A major difference in principle is that we hope to have a self-modifying and more adaptive processing procedure than Kochen, whose solution methods are fixed.

7 Hunt and Hovland's Model

Hunt and Hovland[1] have also produced an information processing model which is equivalent to that of Amarel[2] in some respects as well as Kochen[3] in some other respects. It rests on the assumption that

". . . a useful model of concept learning can be built by programming a procedure for constructing a decision tree."

Hunt and Hovland themselves feel that their work is especially consistent with that of Feigenbaum[4] and Banerji.[5]

Again we would accept the nearness in thought to our model but feel the main differences are with respect to the following two points:

1 No natural language base is included.

2 There is insufficient emphasis on the generating of new heuristics, or of the closest allied process of heuristic modification.

1 E. B. Hunt and C. I. Hovland, Programming a model of human concept formulation, *Proc. Western Joint Computer Conf.*, 1960, 145–155.

2 S. Amarel, An approach to automatic theory formation, In *Principles of Self-organization*, H. von Foerster and Pergamon Press, 1962.

3 M. Kochen, Experimental study of "hypothesis formation" by computer. *Proc. London Sympos. on Information Theory*, 1960.

4 E. A. Feigenbaum, The simulation of verbal learning behaviour. In *Computers and Thoughts*, E. A. Feigenbaum and J. Feldman, (eds), New York: McGraw Hill, 1963.

5 R. B. Banerji, The discription list of concepts, *A.C.M. Journal*, 1962.

6

Induction and Hypothesis Formation

1 Introduction

In this chapter, we will take a closer look at the inductive process. We shall look at it, as with the rest of this monograph, not as a philosopher or mathematician, nor as a psychologist. We shall look at it from the point of view of a model-maker in the process of trying to model human thinking. We shall assume that both induction and deduction, which is to be discussed in the next chapter, are essential features of thinking, and that our problem is to consider how they can be made available to our computer model.

It is convenient to think of induction with respect to various related forms such as Bayes Rule, Inverse Probability, etc. But over and above these corporately developed techniques it is convenient to think of induction as related to sequential processes in an 'on line' manner which is reminiscent of learning *by acquaintance*. It is also convenient to think of induction as "off line" where it is reminiscent of learning *by description*. However this last distinction is not by any means absolute, since inductive learning also takes place by acquaintance in "off line" situations. Let us look at this matter more carefully.

2 Sequential Analysis

The kind of induction concerned with sequential analysis has, on the whole, been less emphasised than that concerned with atemporal induction. Some of the principles involved are relatively simple;

the simplest is perhaps that of collecting conditional probabilities which refer to the sequence of events a, b, ..., n, coupled to some *measure* of their frequency of occurrence:

$$p(a/b) = m_1/n_1$$
$$p(a/bc) = m_2/n_2$$
$$p(ab/c) = m_3/n_3$$
$$p(a/bcd) = m_4/n_4$$
$$\ldots$$
$$\text{etc.}$$

By taking longer and longer samples of sequences we can, by use of the measure of conditional probabilities, refer predictively to events of greater and yet greater length. This is one method of discovering sequential patterns. This method can, of course, be simulated on the computer by a mere collecting, naming and counting operation. By such means we can arrive at new concepts which have been derived from old, and empirical statements and hypotheses derived from concepts.

We should notice that processes or sets of events which are to be thought identical are to be thought so *whether or not they are symbolized*. When symbolized, however, some details are omitted *from the symbolization* (description) and thus in general a problem handled purely in symbolic terms is necessarily less complete than one handled directly by acquaintance in terms of direct, non-verbal, stimuli. Against this we assume that all the most complex and certainly the most abstract problems are inevitably in symbolic form.

We must next ask ourselves whether or not all problems are tractable, in principle, in terms of such sequential methods. The answer is uncertain, but for human beings most problems come within the logical hypothetico-deductive (or inductive-deductive) and linguistic complex, and in principle, we can see how these could be handled in a computer program. The fact that all the events (names) may have been collected before induction takes place does not destroy the sequential nature of the problem. From the computer viewpoint, we are now considering what is sometimes called *heuristic generation*.

We should mention here a distinction made by Neisser,[1] since it runs close to the distinction made between sequential and non-sequential analysis. Neisser talks of sequential and multiple processes.

[1] F. H. George, Inductive logic on computers. A paper submitted to the Conference of Computer Science at Liepzig, 1968.

He is emphasising, as were we, the on line analysis of sequences, as opposed to collected evidence seen as-a-whole.

The reader should bear in mind just this sort of distinction, and remember the multiple processes are those that involve Gestalts.

3   Examples of Heuristic Generation

Given an ordered set of numbers (i, j, . . ., n), our problem is to derive certain general features, if any exist, that draw attention either to similarities between (different) subsets, or to differences between (similar) subsets. When, and if, we give meaning (add "semantic rules") to the members of the sets, interpreting them say as "number of people living in Amsterdam", "number of women in the world", etc., we can proceed along more specific lines of search. Before we do this we should consider the general (abstract) case, where the members of the set can be ordered and the sets themselves can be ordered.

We shall name the sets S_o, S_l, . . ., S_r and use, where needed, the superfixes i, j, . . ., n to identify the item of the set which is used for ordering, or for whatever operation is needed. Sets with the same values as elements constitute one example of what we mean, since they represent two different ways of referring to the same set. They are, in fact, synonyms. e.g. $S_7{}^{i\,=\,8} = S_8{}^{i\,=\,8}$. Note superfix gives number of members and the suffix is part of the name of the set. These sets can be sorted and classified, to see, for example if they always contain other similarities or differences, e.g.

$$(S_7{}^{i\,=\,8} = S_8{}^{i\,=\,8}) \cap (S_7{}^{k\,=\,13} = S_8{}^{k\,=\,13})$$

or

$$(S_7{}^{i\,=\,8} = S_8{}^{i\,=\,8}) \cap (S_7{}^{k-1\,=\,2} = S_8{}^{k-1\,=\,2})$$

In fact we can, in principle, use the method of differences, or other methods for summing series, and set up, say, *difference equations* to represent some of the general principles representing similarities or differences in a series or a sequence, which are ordered sets.

A second class of analysis by sets occurs if we partition the sets. We can ask now whether specific subsets are significantly different from each other and statistical methods, such as the *Difference between Means, Significance of a Single Mean*, etc, occur as likely methods to use. We could though ask whether such subsets are *correlated.* A whole host of statistical methods now suggest themselves, as well as simpler heuristic equivalents. The undertaking, in general, is indeed, as in the first case, hopelessly uneconomic unless we have some starting "insight" or "heuristic".

If we examine all the possible relationships implied by the above two cases alone, for even fairly small sets of sets $\sum_{i=1}^{30} S_i$, say, it is clearly an uneconomic undertaking. So as in ordinary scientific research, we formulate hypotheses (heuristics) and test them by the means used above.

The third type of analysis which is obviously relevant is of a stochastic kind (see Appendix 4). We can consider sequences 1, 2, . . ., n at a time of either whole sets or any of the subsets.

Such conditional probabilistic stochastic processes are called Finite Markov Chains. It should be added that in the example of maze running which uses conditional probability tables and a tree-structure we talk of the simplest example of a whole family of problems, which can be made more and more complex, by the following conditions:

1 The choice of a route and its cost may itself change as a function of use.

2 A deterministic problem involving costs, say, may be a probabilistic problem based on uncertainties.

3 Information may be incomplete, where even the probabilities are not all known.

The Dynamic Programming technique, which is in a sense a generalization on stochastic processes, uses the Calculus of Variations for a continuous deterministic case, and Dynamic Programming for the Stochastic Case. Where the game is a Minimax procedure, as in Games Against Nature, the problem reduces to that of a standard linear programme.

We shall next try and provide a link between the arguments leading by way of concept formation to hypothesis formation (Chapter 5) and the arguments about induction given in the present chapter.

4   Hypothesis Formation and Induction

Having concepts and names for the classes to which they belong, or for their collective properties (Chapter 6), we can, as we have seen, conjoin such concepts and express them as empirical propositions.

We can say, for example, that "some men are tall" and provided only that the class words 'men' and 'tall' are sufficiently clearly defined, then we can acquire evidence to support (or not) such a proposition.

Evidence can be of the form, "I know some men (one man) and they are (he is) tall", and this is sufficient. If the proposition had been "all men are tall", then, of course, such supporting evidence would be insufficient, and only one short man would be sufficient to disprove the hypothesis.

The problem we have in mind in this chapter is primarily that of performing *induction* on a computer, and relating that inductive process specifically to hypothesis formation. We also need to link the work explicitly to our computer programs. We shall attempt no more here than a discussion of the programming of the simplest examples, with a brief discussion of how these examples might be reasonably followed up.

We can continue to think of the fairly rough distinction we have made between spatial and temporal extrapolation. So, to take the temporal sequence first, we may consider a set of events depicted by the letters $\overline{A}, \overline{B}, \ldots, \overline{N}$. We hope, parenthetically, that no confusion will arise over notation because capital letters are sometimes used for functions or operators in the logical description. So we may consider first of all the conditional probabilities of one event with respect to the next, e.g.

$$p(\overline{A}/\overline{B})$$

is the probability of $\overline{A}$ given $\overline{B}$ and we may supply a measure such as:

$$(p(\overline{A}/\overline{B}) = m(= \tfrac{3}{4} \text{ say})$$

where $\tfrac{3}{4}$ is simply the Laplacian probability of $\overline{A}$ occurring, given that $\overline{B}$ has occurred; all this being in the light of past experience.

Consider the sequence of events depicted by the following symbols:

ABCADABCABCADABCABABACACABDBACABAA

we can construct a set of conditional probability tables for events of length 2 (over only *two* successive events in time) as follows:

F

	$\overline{A}$	$\overline{B}$	$\overline{C}$	$\overline{D}$
$\overline{A}$	1/14	8/14	3/14	2/14
$\overline{B}$	4/9	0	4/9	1/9
$\overline{C}$	7/7	0	0	0
$\overline{D}$	2/3	1/3	0	0

Table 1

This clearly implies that given $\overline{C}$, for example, $\overline{A}$ may definitely be expected to follow.

From such a table we can, albeit tentatively, draw conclusions about necessary and contingent relations, e.g.

> Given $\overline{C}$, $\overline{A}$ *necessarily* follows, and
> given $\overline{D}$, $\overline{A}$ *contingently* follows,
> twice as often as $\overline{B}$.

We can also consider events three at a time so we could have, based on the same events, tables which, given $\overline{A}$, $\overline{B}$, $\overline{C}$ or $\overline{D}$, shows the frequency of $\overline{A}\overline{A}$, $\overline{A}\overline{B}$, . . . etc. following. Also given $\overline{A}\overline{A}$, $\overline{A}\overline{B}$, . . . etc the frequency of $\overline{A}$, $\overline{B}$, . . . etc following could be tabulated.

From here we can go on to consider events of length 4, 5, . . ., etc.

But let us merely emphasize that this form of sequential analysis is appropriate to conditional probability tables of length n, and view the whole matter from a different point of view. The second point of view involves many-channelled inputs, and the occurrence of individuals.

Suppose we draw up a 4-channel tape for successive instants t_0, t_1, . . ., t_7 inclusive, as follows:

t_0	t_1	t_2	t_3	t_4	t_5	t_6	t_7
	$\overline{A}$		$\overline{A}$	$\overline{A}$		$\overline{A}$	$\overline{A}$
	$\overline{B}$	$\overline{B}$	$\overline{B}$		$\overline{B}$	$\overline{B}$	$\overline{B}$
$\overline{C}$	$\overline{C}$		$\overline{C}$			$\overline{C}$	$\overline{C}$
$\overline{D}$		$\overline{D}$				$\overline{D}$	

Table 2

We now see how the concept of *individuals* arises. It is clear that $(\overline{A}\overline{B}\overline{C})$ could be a part of a coherent whole. So that in the three appearances of $(\overline{A}\overline{B}\overline{C})$, all the features occur together. The events $\overline{A}$, $\overline{B}$ and $\overline{C}$ here represent the properties x, y and z which are three appearances of some individual. This seems to be the case on the grounds that they always occur together.

Let us consider, as an example, a dog. A dog is an individual with properties such as being *four-legged*, *tailed*, *two-eyed*, etc. . . . Name these properties x, y, z, etc, and then we can think of (x, y, z) as a simplified description of an individual such as a dog.

In the same way as a dog can present itself, so the class of all *objects*, such as *chairs*, *tables*, *pictures*, etc., can be exemplified. The problem, which can be treated for expository purposes, in a simplified form involving only an unrealistically few properties, can be dealt with in terms as complex or as simple as are made necessary by circumstances.

The argument is that *successive* events incorporate sets 1, 2, . . ., n, at a time, and also *simultaneous* events incorporate sets of 1, 2, . . ., m, at a time, involving specific sets (or individuals) which are the basic material of inductive inference.

The next stage is to show that such inductive arguments as: "given A, B will follow with probability p" or "given A and B, the probability is that the individual K, where K is the set (x, y, z) is present, has probability p". Our next step must be to show how a general purpose digital computer deals with such matters.

We use a three-address computer with basic order code as follows:

ADD/A/B/C which means "add the number in B to the number in A, and put the result in C".

SUB/A/B/C/ is the same as the add instruction but is concerned with subtracting b from a, where A(a) and B(b), i.e. address A contains number a and number b is in register with address B.

MUL/A/B/C involves multiplying a by b.

DIV/A/B/C involves dividing a by b.

JUM/A/B/C means "If $a \geqslant b$, then jump to instruction in C".

LOD/A/B/C means "load A words starting at B and take the next instruction from C".

PRI/A/B/C means "print A words starting at B and take the next instruction from C".

STO/A/B/C/ means "absolute stop".

COP/A/B/C which means "copy contents of A into B and take the next instruction from C".

Note that we are now using the capital letters A, B, ..., N in another sense, as addresses of locations in a computer store.

Let us suppose we have an environment given by table 2. We must also suppose that we wish to identify an object $\alpha = (xy)$ and discover whether or not it has (always) the property z.

Let us allocate stores such that:

$$200(t_0)$$

$$201(t_1)$$

$$202(t_2)$$

$$\cdots$$

etc.

We have instructions which are designed to achieve the following:

Find out when xy occurs and find out whether z always occurs with xy or not.

So we need to use the instructions:

Compare input with xy, is it the same or different; if the same, test for z, and record how often z is present with xy.

Let us then code x, y, z and W as 001, 010, 011 and 100 and now plant xy as 001010 in location 300 say, and plant z as 011 in 301. We now use the TRY instruction, TRY/A/B/C meaning

"If a = b, then take the next instruction from C"

where A(a), B(b), which means that a is the contents of the register with address A, and b is the contents of the register with address B.

Note, we are here also using lower case alphabetic letters in a second sense as the contents of computer locating.

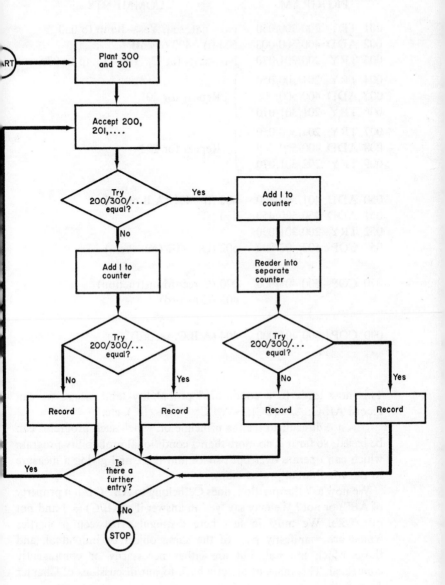

Our program is:

PROGRAM		COMMENTS
001 TRY	200/300/050	No—nat. seq. Yes—Jump to 050
002 ADD	400/500/003	500 (l) 400 (event)
003 TRY	200/301/070	No—tests for C_I. Yes—Jump to 070
004 TRY	201/300/050	
005 ADD	400/500/006	Repeat for 201
006 TRY	201/301/070	
007 TRY	202/300/050	
008 ADD	400/500/009	Repeat for 202
009 TRY	202/301/070	
. . .		etc
050 ADD	401/500/400	500 (l) 401 (A.B record)
051 ADD	450/500/450	450 (O)
052 TRY	200/301/090	
053 COP	502/402/000	502 (O) 402 (mil event)
. . .		
070 COP	500/403/000	070 (C record instruction)
		403 (C record)
. . .		
090 COP	500/404/000	404 (A.B.C. record)
. . .		

This now leads to a conditional probability table where we can record $\overline{A}/\overline{B}\overline{C}$; $\overline{A}/\sim(\overline{B}\overline{C})$; $\sim\overline{A}/\overline{B}\overline{C}$; $\sim/\overline{A}\sim(\overline{B}\overline{C})$, etc.

It is not difficult to see the principle on which such programs can be based; so far it is no more than a conditional probability program which can operate over both space and time, and giving a measure to the conditional probabilities.

We now ask the question, does $\overline{C}$ "belong to $\overline{A}\overline{B}$" ("is it a property of $\overline{A}\overline{B}$") or not? We may say 'yes' in answer if $p(\overline{A}\overline{B}/\overline{C}) = 1$ and not otherwise. We must in fact here distinguish between properties which are manifestly part of the same object or individual, and those which are not, but are either necessarily or contingently connected. This takes us directly back to our discussions of Chapter 5.

Our programming technique so far merely counts properties, and it must also identify individuals. So it should *name* xyz as α, for example, where

$$\alpha = df . \text{xyz}$$

and where *df.* means "by definition".

In assessing whether an object is an individual we shall need conventions, since we might for example be unsure as to whether the bell on a bicycle is *a part of* the bicycle or not. We might indeed have to change our views as to what composes an individual and what does not. However, while this is a point to remember; it is also one that can fairly easily be solved in any particular context.

So far, we have talked of induction in the computer context as identifiable with the collecting in some form of conditional probabilities; we must now go beyond this to the more general interpretative statements which we know are also a vital part of induction. Look at some more examples:

"All cats are white"	. . . (9)
"All cats meet in Bristol in June"	. . . (10)
"All Welsh people are born with two eyes and two ears"	. . . (11)

etc.

Our computer methods are adequate to this new purpose, since, if we use the semantic rules as follows:

> Cats = a, white = b, Bristol = c,
> June = n, Welsh people = e, eyes = p,
> ears = r;

then we have sentence forms

a.b.	. . . (12)
a.c.n	. . . (13)
$e.p(2).r(2)$	. . . (14)

These are trivial examples, but serve to·remind us that properties (and individuals) occur together in space or time as a basis for an induction.

Our problem is now not only to develop methods for performing an inductive check, but also to develop methods for both expressing that induction in language, as well as interpreting other people's inductions in language. We must now look at the matter as a linguistic problem akin to that previously discussed by the author.[1] This takes us into the field of what we have called "Non-Sequential Analysis".

5 Non-Sequential Analysis and Heuristic Methods

In discussions on thinking, we tend to consider the creative activity of deriving hypotheses or "seeing" appropriate deductive inferences that can be made in a problem-solving context. Whereas simple learning, like habit formation, can be thought of as occurring sequentially, we do not as frequently draw attention to the sequential processes in thinking or problem-solving. Perhaps the main reason for this is that whereas we may acquire the information as a temporally ordered process, the basis for such inductions as are made are usually independent of how the information is collected. Let us look for a moment at some well known work in this field.

Newell, Shaw and Simon[2] made a detailed study of what they called *creative thinking* which dealt with those aspects of problem-solving which required originality, as opposed to explanation, definition, remembering, etc., all of which come into the day-to-day problem-solver's activities.

Their work has great importance because they were able to show by heuristic programming techniques how short cuts in routes to goals (solutions) could be achieved by assumptions that facilitated the problem-solving process.

The manner of approach is simple enough in principle, and we can illustrate the method which is called the *heuristic principle*. If you are an architect and asked to design a building and the building is intended for use as offices, then you can omit consideration of previous designs for private houses, garages, etc, whereas when performing the task algorithmically, you might consider *every* possible building type however irrelevant.

Newell, Shaw and Simon also refer to stages in problem-solving involving *incubation, illumination*, etc, and these can all be simulated in some measure on the computer.

Newell, Shaw and Simon used *solution generators*, trial-and-error

[1] F. H. George, Inductive logic on computers. A paper submitted to the Conference of Computer Science at Liepzig, 1968.
[2] A. Newell, J. C. Shaw and H. A. Simon, Elements in a theory of human problem solving, *Psychol. Rev.*, 1958, *65*, 151–66.

learning and then the formation of hypotheses, often involving working backwards from the solution (deducing subgoals from goals) where the problem was, for example, to find some proof. They used *verifying processes* to justify their steps and in this they made a distinction that parallels Reichenbach's[1] distinction between the context of discovery and the context of justification; this we have already mentioned.

The author's own research differs from that of Newell, Shaw and Simon in its use of heuristics. They were concerned with simulating principles for theorem proving, and they used the human-like means of substitution, etc. We are more concerned with the delineation (through language) of a problem for which appropriate heuristics have to be sought (hypothesis formation by induction) and/or adapted to the needs of the situation.

Heuristics are generalized rules-of-thumb or hypotheses and can be used in various ways. Newell, Shaw and Simon simulated the operations of the human problem-solver, but Samuel[2] synthesized his heuristics by a set of polynomials and thus the parameters could be adjusted by experience from which appropriate heuristics were, in effect, selected. Tonge[3] used heuristics to solve aspects of the line balancing problem, and the adaptivity of the heuristics was essentially pre-planned; a somewhat similar procedure was followed by Burstall.[4]

As distinct from these piecemeal efforts, we wish to see heuristics in use in all these ways, operating *together*, and heuristic generation to occur as appropriate to the solution of a problem.

From the computer viewpoint, heuristics are like sub-routines in a computer program, and they can be edited or strung together to form new heuristics, or what we have called plans.

We must remember to distinguish between adaptive and non-adaptive heuristics. This in fact reflects a distinction that is similar to that between "taking a set of hypotheses" as opposed to testing

[1] H. Reichenbach, *Experience and Prediction*, University of Chicago Press, 1938.

[2] A. L. Samuel, Some studies in machine learning using the game of checkers. In *Computers and Thought*, E. A. Feigenbaum and J. Feldman (eds.), New York: McGraw Hill, 1963, 71–105.

[3] F. M. Tonge, Summary of a heuristic line balancing procedure, In *Computers and Thought*, E. A. Feigenbaum and J. Feldman (eds)., New York: McGraw Hill, 1963, 168–90.

[4] R. M. Burstall, A heuristic method for a job scheduling problem. Experimental Programming Unit, Edinburgh, 1966.

and, if necessary, modifying those hypotheses as a result of circumstances; or indeed even setting out "new" hypotheses.

Relatively fixed numerical heuristics are already commonplace in computing; they include all mathematical models, such as those used in fields such as Sales Estimation or Market Research.

The ability to adapt heuristics implies the ability to construct new plans which in turn implies the ability to set up and re-organize sub routines in computer programs.

It is in these terms that we see problem-solving as a synthetic undertaking. Problem-solving is the ability to construct or reconstruct sub routines to solve problems and learn new sub routines by experience as circumstances demand; this is done especially by way of verbal description.

This synthetic approach would be of limited value were it not regarded as experimental; the whole purpose is to write and run such computer programs to discover the extent to which the programs do in fact synthesize, perhaps even simulate, the conditions in which we are interested.

Heuristics are essentially the same as hypotheses, and heuristic programming, and especially heuristic generation, is analogous to hypotheses learning. Adaptive programming and conventional programming provide examples of learning, all the way down to the level of fixed responding.

We are careful now to distinguish the process of discovering an induction (e.g. counting, Bayes Rule) and the inductive statement itself (the inductive generalization). The first is a type of curve-fitting or pattern recognition operation and we must distinguish between the method by which we arrive at the "best-fit", and the formula which we actually adopt as a result of the fitting. This is rather like our rough distinction between sequential analysis (collecting the data) and non-sequential analysis (formulating the heuristic).

Now let us turn to the problem of induction as it has been tackled more traditionally.

6 Induction

To make our underlying assumptions clearer, it should be said that we are assuming that inside the organism we have the apparatus of language, which is built up through experience, like other learned skills. We assume that language, as we grow up, is increasingly used to refer to our experiences of the external world, and operates together with certain "physiological" or "psychological" occurrences called "images".

Language is both a description of, and also part of, since it is self-referential, the internal conceptual model (schema); we have an internal model of the world about us *and* of ourselves, and we as humans are assumed to be aware of words and images often in complex associations. At this level the "mental processes" are to be thought of as fairly crude and to depend on associative principles. But underlying these *molar* "mental processes" are the molecular processes which make it possible.

The molecular processes are all assumed to be activities of the nervous system. We are certainly unaware of our neurons firing in their various complex patterns, but there is reason to believe that this is what is actually occurring. The effect of these complex firing patterns is to suggest a mechanism which worked *as if* it were a sophisticated mathematical process; it seems reasonable therefore to try to both synthesize and simulate it. We can here use these same mathematical processes for both operations; they have become, in effect, descriptions of a fraction of the nervous system. The nervous system at this stage could be called 'conceptual' rather than real, although this is a difference which can only be one of degree.

We shall not discuss deduction[1] and the various work in theorem-proving until Chapter 7, since the problem of deduction will be already sufficiently understood to enable anyone to grasp a large part of its relation to thinking; such an argument though hardly applies to induction.

[1] J. L. Darlington, A Comit program for the Davis-Putnam algorithm. *Res. Lab. Electron., Mech. Transl. Grp., M.I.T.*, Cambridge, Mass., 1962.

B. Raphael, SIR, a computer program for semantic information retrieval. *Fall Joint Comput. Conf., 25*, 1964.

F. H. George, Hypothesis confirmation on a digital computer. Paper read at Bionics Conference Dayton, Ohio, 1966.

H. Wang, Proving theorems by pattern recognition. *I. Comm. Ass. of Comp. Mach.*, 1960, *3*, 220–34.

A. Newell, J. C. Shaw and H. A. Simon, The theorem-proving machine. In *Computers and Thought*, E. Feigenbaum and J. Feldman (eds.), New York: McGraw Hill, 1963.

7 Belief Formation

We shall now consider *belief formation*[1] as the psychological
process which is subserved by induction. We are thinking here of
beliefs in the same sense as hypotheses (some of which are heuristics)[2] and being in need of confirmation by empirical evidence.
We write:

$$c(h,e)$$

to be read "the degree of confirmation of the hypothesis h by
evidence e" and we will generally identify this with some value p
such that $0 \leq p \leq 1$, so that

$$c(h,e) = p$$

It is clear that evidence in the objective sense will not always
apply to our personal beliefs, but will in general apply to rational
beliefs, since this is really what we mean by the words 'evidence' and
'rational'; but we shall need to state some satisfactory criteria for
'rational beliefs'. In doing so, we are moving into well-trod territory,
and we must be careful to point out again that our motives in doing
so are not those of mathematicians, philosophers and logicians who
may be interested primarily in mathematical generality or episte-
mological clarity. Nor are they those of the psychologist who is
strictly interested in the simulation of human behaviour with a view
to its prediction. Our interest comes somewhere in between the three
and involves the pragmatic consideration of acquiring realistic
humanlike reasoning, but not necessarily as humans do it; in other
words we are interested in synthesis as a starting point for our
simulation.

We shall devote the next section to a very brief summary of the
difficulties met so far in the fields of induction and inductive logic.

8 Inductive Logic

Inductive logic is a system for providing both evidence for and
confirmation of inductive inferences. If we say

'All dogs are blue'   . . . (1)

---

[1] F. H. George and J. H. Handlon, Towards a general theory of behaviour,
Methodos, 1955, *1*, 25–44.

[2] A. L. Samuel, Some studies in machine learning using the game of checkers.
In *Computers and Thought*, E. A. Feigenbaum and J. Feldman (eds.), New York,
McGraw Hill, 1963, 71–105.

then if I have seen 256 dogs all of which were blue and no dog that is non-blue, this constitutes evidence to support (1) above.

Difficulties occur in inductive logic for various reasons. The first difficulty arises because some people have felt that seeing a non-blue non-dog is also evidence for (1).

So we must ask ourselves does a particular herring being red in any way confirm that all dogs are blue?

We shall waste no time over the more technical points[1] of inductive logic, but say merely that a certain support, primarily for syntactical reasons, has been found for the view that such statements as "All dogs are blue" is confirmed by such statements as

$$\text{"Most herrings are red"} \quad \ldots (2)$$

We shall also say, however, following the famous Nicode's condition that (2) is irrelevant to (1). We should mention that the problem of relevance as met above is also involved with the use of material implication. Material implication is defined in traditional symbolic logic as follows:

$$a \supset b = \text{df.} \sim a \lor b \quad \ldots (3)$$

which is intended to be interpreted as "if ... then - - -". This use may be a defensible definition of material implication in a syntactical theory, but entails that, where a and b are interpreted as statements, one statement may imply another statement even though they are not in any way connected with each other, i.e. are irrelevant to each other. This is certainly contrary to human argument and is essentially the same as the defect, for our purposes, which we observe in universal confirmation.

We shall now say, what was said earlier, that a statement S_1 *is relevant to* another statement S_2 if it has a common subject or predicate or if it can be *linked* by a common subject or predicate.[2]

According to such a notation of relevance any statement *directly* relevant to (1) must be one of the following form

$$\text{"All dogs are - - -"} \quad \ldots (3)$$

$$\text{"- - - are blue"} \quad \ldots (4)$$

[1] See a series of papers by C. H. von Wright, P. Suppes, Max Black and R., Hilpinen in *Aspects of Inductive Logic*, J. Hintikka and P. Suppes (eds.), Amsterdam: North Holland Publ. Co.

[2] F. H. George, Hypothesis confirmation on a digital computer, *Symp. on Bionics*, Dayton, Ohio, 1966.

and similar statements prefixed by the existential operator, i.e. which refer to a class with at least one member, rather than to a universal class. Furthermore, any statement is *indirectly* relevant to (1) if it has a form which be traced by the same associative principle such as in (3) and (4). For example "All cats are white" is indirectly relevant to (1) if there exist a finite number of statements of a similar kind linked to it, one at least of which involves the terms 'dog' or 'blue'.

The other vital point about relevance is that of *causal* relations. If, for example, a species of dogs such as some wild dogs are thought to be biologically related to domesticated dogs, and if they are all blue, then this might be thought to be confirmatory evidence for (1). So we must accept the fact that there may exist causal chains which are not necessarily descriptively or logically complete, although in principle they are capable of being completed, and which may be relevant to our purpose. It is assumed, of course, that all such statements as (3) and (4) will not be on the same level of generality; this does not effect the argument.

All that has been said so far is hardly likely to settle many problems in the field of confirmation, but at least it clarifies our own starting position. We shall have a feasible model with which to start our computer model, and by virtue of extensive testing in computer programming we shall be prepared to make changes as, when and if they become necessary, i.e. according to the pragmatic test of whether or not such programs work well enough or not.

We shall certainly want throughout these computer operations to be able to make use of all known statistical techniques and this implies that we need to include a *measure*, wherever this is possible, and use some concept such as "weight of evidence". Without this we shall be in principle incapable of using correlations, t-tests, etc., which are most desirable. We must repeat here that we shall also need to write *recognition programs* which specify when some specific technique is called for. Such a step is vital to the autonomous "machine decision-taker".

We are not, though, concerned here with showing how frequency theory statistics relates to probability theory, any more than we are trying to show how mathematics follows from recursive function theory and set theory. We are merely concerned to remind the reader of the vital importance of linguistically based corporately developed methods. From the synthetic point of view, the introduction of statistical methods implies no more than having the appropriate standard computer programs available and having the capacity to recognize (pattern recognition) when they are needed, although the problem of recognition must necessarily itself be heuristic and is, of course, inductive.

Briefly, we shall now deal with some other related matters. We should separate *credibility* from *probability*.[1] We will say that credibility includes probability, and that whenever a statement can be supported by (or confirmed by) an objective (relevant) probability then it comes within our concept of confirmation. It is clear, as a matter of human psychology, that human beings often regard statements as credible on non-objective bases (even indeed though they may be correct) and will sometimes support credible statements on objective probabilistic bases (even though they be incorrect).

This is inevitable and we accept this as true of any system which is to operate under conditions of uncertainty. We shall however use confirmation as a necessary condition for acceptance, and in general say that the extent of one is proportional to the extent of the other, subject to "risk analysis" being used.

We shall say that inductive generalizations are confirmed by other specific methods such as Bayes Rule, stimulus sampling, Markov Chains, etc, and that this coupled with work on Explanation and Factual Support are all part and parcel of the justificatory process.

We should say here that we are tempted to draw a distinction between confirming theories or hypotheses on one hand and providing a basis for decision-making on the other. This distinction though is in some measure contaminated by our other main distinction between formal (normative) and factual (behavioursitic) accounts of decision-making. This is especially important if we follow Suppes[2] and compare concept formation as a means of manufacturing new concepts from an *infinite* possible base.[3] (See Chapter 5) with Bayes decision taking which presupposes a whole *finite* universe of possibilities from the start; these are similar to examples of growth and fixed automata respectively.

[1] B. Russell, *Human knowledge; its scope and limits*, George Allen and Unwin, 1948.

[2] P. Suppes, See a series of papers by G. H. von Wright, P. Suppes, Max Black and R. Hilpinen in *Aspects of Inductive Logic*, J. Hintikka and P. Suppes (eds.) Amsterdam: North Holland Publ. Co.

[3] R. B. Banerji, A language for pattern recognition, *Pattern Recognition Society*. (In the press)

F. H. George, Hypothesis confirmation on a digital computer, *Symp. on Bionics*, Dayton, Ohio, 1966.

The above distinction is important on grounds of utility, since it seems that in using heuristic computer methods, the stimulus-sampling, Markov net type of approach, which allows easily for the addition of new concepts, is also more economic to use. This point has been well demonstrated by Suppes.[1]

The relative importance of arguing either from a true (certain) or probabilistic datum, is another point worth mentioning. Clearly no empirical data are certain and although we could argue, that a datum could be a proposition that "has some degree of rational credibility on its own account, independently of any argument derived from other proposition",[2] this is not an idea easily used in practice, nor is it obviously useful. This though is hardly an important point since our own view is more nearly that of C. S. Peirce, to the effect that we have a set of more or less coherent and more or less confirmed beliefs, which we regard, in their totality, as our knowledge. We then use this "knowledge" to provide a basis for inference-making. We will accept therefore probabilistic data as a basis for induction and as a result must knowingly expose ourselves to the danger of drawing false or improbable conclusions. Now finally let us return to the computer context.

Confirmation in Computers

In the computer situation heuristics can be manufactured by induction, either by "hunch" or by description. Whichever way the heuristic is acquired, and we have discussed many such methods, we are also involved, as we have said, explicitly in confirmation.

First of all, we may have heuristics which refer to events with "low risk" and these can be confirmed in experience, at leisure, provided always urgency is also low. If urgency is high and if risk is high then confirmation must be urgently replaced by computer simulation of the events. This, of course, eliminates the other two categories where urgency is low and risk is high, or urgency is high and risk low, where behaviour may be trial-and-error or on the basis of hypothesis, and where action is immediately needed in the latter case, and where behaviour must be simulated, although it may be done at leisure in the former.

Let us then assume a set of four hypotheses or heuristics H_1, H_2,

1 P. Suppes, See footnote 1, p. 93.
2 B. Russell, *Human knowledge; its scope and limits*, George Allen and Unwin, 1948.

H_3, H., arrived at by description. We must now go through the minimum steps of attempted confirmation.

We have sources and their reliability, etc, stored, so let us consider the simplest case of checking source X's past reliability.

PROGRAM	COMMENTS
B_{30} (Source X record)	Sources and their reliability records register from B_{20} onwards, made up of statements S_1, S_2, . . ., S_n.
D_1 (S_1), D_1 (S_2), . . .	
B_1 (S_1), B_2 (S_2), . . .	

Message M_1 includes source symbol X (coded 461) and codeword X comes just before STOP (999).

Decode 461	B_{50} (461)
A60 . Try $B_{20}/B_{50}/B_{80}$	
A61 . Try $B_{21}/B_{50}/A_{80}$ . . .	
A70 . Try $B_{30}/B_{50}/A_{80}$ . . .	Carry on until B_{30} reached.
A_{80} COP $B_{30}/B_{51}/A_{81}$	
A_{81} . . .	B_{30} (17, 24)

If no other consideration arises, and risk analysis provided a 50 : 50 chance confidence level, C_1 now behaves as if H_1, H_2, H_3, H_4 are true.

But we must now move to the next test which we shall no longer give in the form of a symbolic program, since the methods are now sufficiently obvious even to those readers less familiar with computer programming.

Our two brief examples of symbolic machine code programming can be summarized in computer terms as:

$$COU (x, y, c)$$

where x and y are two properties counted (COU) as either occurring or not occurring together. We can add such other symbols c as are needed to identify relevant storage registers. Similarly reliability can be called:

$$REL (k, l, m)$$

while we leave k, l, and m as dummy parameters.

In exactly the same way we can set up sub routines or procedures which identify *motive* of source.

$$MOT (k, l, m)$$

G

means "compare name of circumstance, k say, with each suspect circumstance starting at l, and if none are found, accept probability weighting and proceed to m".

Tests for consistency can be similarly provided, so we use compiler word:

$$CON (k, l, m)$$

where k, l, and m are again dummy parameters.

Finally we should say that the aim is to use all these procedures in a well defined compiler language which is currently being constructed. The language is in list processing form and is comparable to I.P.L.$\overline{V}$.[1]

We may expect such statements in the compiler as

> CON (k, l, m)
> If NO, ASSERT WEIGHT
> If YES, INVERT WEIGHT

where 'assert' and 'invert' mean the acceptance of some probability m/n, say, and the inverting is the changing of that probability to the probability n-m/n; more sophisticated transformations are clearly possible.

The aim of this research is ultimately to provide a compiler language in which programs can be written for logical linguistic, heuristic and confirmatory operations. This Chapter has attempted to provide a part and only a part of the total picture.

Let us remind ourselves at this point that our aim is to provide precisely programmed heuristics, meta-heuristics and heuristic generators which are embedded in a background of deductive and inductive logic. The task is to make plausible starting programs and then let them run in an environment on a self-correcting basis in the hope that we can generate models which accurately simulate different features of rational human behaviour.

In the next chapter we consider logic—especially deductive logic—in the computer context.

[1] A. Newell, *Information Processing Language V Manual*, Englewood Cliffs, New Jersey: Prentice Hall, 1961.

7

Logic

1 Introduction

This chapter gives a short survey of inference making on a computer. We are mainly concerned here with *deduction* but will finish the chapter by providing a link with induction.

The purpose of this chapter is to make clear the nature of logical inference making in a form suitable for computers, and to relate the procedure to that of natural language computing which will be described in the next chapter. The emphasis is on the logic itself and some mention is made of the experimental programs which have been written.[1]

2 The Technical Problem

The first question to be dealt with is about logical inference and its relation to natural language. What part here do the established formal calculi such as Boolean Algebra, the Propositional Calculi, the Functional Calculi and the Calculus of Relations play in such inference making?

We shall bear in mind that there are various other calculi and other combinatorial logics which may be relevant; an example of such a combinational logic is the λ-calculus. We shall also bear in mind that calculi for formal symbolic systems provide the possibility of more than one interpretation. We must remember that such logical systems are permissive; they say what inferences *can* be made, but

---

[1] F. H. George, The Development of Semantics Machines, *Cybernetics*, 1967, No. 3, pp. 145–72.

do not say that some *must* be made. What decides which inferences must be made in a humanlike model depends upon the *goal* and what is *relevant* to that goal. In other words if we need, for example, to supply evidence to support a hypothesis, then we are told, in effect, what inferences must be made. This is the major point about relevance which was mentioned in the last chapter.

It is clear that Boolean Algebra plays an important part in natural language inference making. Its effectiveness depends upon the transitivity of class inclusion (or implication) i.e.

$$(a \rightarrow b) \cap ((b \rightarrow c) . (a \rightarrow c))$$

where $\rightarrow$ means "implies", in the ordinary sense of "If --- then ...", which is not necessarily the same as $\supset$ which is interpreted as "material implication", $\cap$ means conjunction as usual and a, b and c are classes. These classes can be interpreted, under certain conditions as the terms of the syllogism.

The syllogism represents a class of logical arguments for which an algorithm is available in the form of syllogistic rules. There are also other sets of relations between propositions which lead to the making of logical inferences, such as the Aristotelian Sorites, the Goclenian Sorites, and many other collections of propositions, which permit the making of valid inferences.

Let us look at a non-syllogistic argument:

> Irishmen are taller than Portuguese
> Portuguese are taller than Italians
> therefore
> Irishmen are taller than Italians

symbolically:

$$b \langle a$$
$$c \langle b \text{ and therefore}$$
$$c \langle a$$

Let us call the phrase "... is taller than ---" by the name T, and we must ask what T entails. T entails the height of a, say, is greater than b (in every case, i.e. for all members of the classes a and b). But we now see the word *height* needs definition, i.e. we need, of course, *Semantic Rules*. These include *definitions* and *entailments*.

We can define 'height' as follows:

k (k $\subset$ a) has *height* x', if when standing, he is placed against a ruler and a plane tangential to his head top and orthogonal to the ruler reads x′.

We now need of course, to define 'ruler', 'tangential', 'orthogonal', 'head', etc. Somehow we have got away from the purely logical, and into Semantics and we have here some problems to solve.

Boolean Algebra, or the calculus of sets (or classes) is, as we saw above, fundamental to much logical inference, but not sufficient to allow inferences to be drawn where the *meaning of terms* is vital to the inference drawing.

We can next construct an axiomatic system and derive the consequences of our axioms. This leads to "compound" formulae which may be collectively true or false, and therefore theorems or not, even though they may all be properly formed according to our rules of formation. It is convenient to use a categorization of linguistic logic[1] which divides sentences into the following groups:

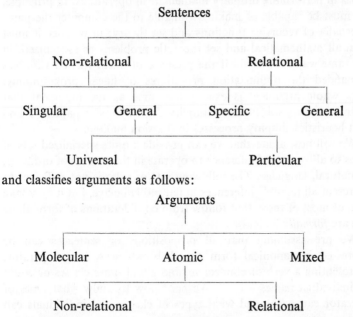

and classifies arguments as follows:

The distinction between Relational and Non-relational sentences and arguments is of great importance. The use of relational words defines a relational sentence. Here a subject is related to an object by verbs such as 'belongs to', 'contains', 'is shorter than', etc.

[1] G. B. Keen, *Language and Reasoning*, Van Nostrand, 1961.

Singular and general are contrasted by examples such as "it is blue" (singular), "some old people are kind" (general (as opposed to singular)).

Molecular arguments are dependent on necessary truth or entailment, e.g.

> "Some wives are kind
> implies
> some kind people are wives."

Non-relational atomic arguments are called syllogistic and have an algorithm, and Relational atomic arguments are the most complex, and an axiomatic system capable of depicting them would certainly take us into the realms of the Functional Calculi.

We should note here, that Propositional and Functional Calculi are basic to mathematics, but no mathematician argues from such bases in performing ordinary mathematical operations. In principle, we must be capable of making available to the computer the paraphernalia of recursive functions and set theory; in practice it must treat all mathematical and set theoretic problems as specialized, in the same way as it would if the presence of linear related variables demanded the optimization procedures of linear programming. This whole argument is exactly the same as the argument that definition and substitution simplify descriptions (Chapter 5) and that heuristics simplify processes in decision making.

We will now argue that we can provide a quite specialized sets of rules to allow *logical* inference to operate in the context of ordinary, or natural, language. The following sets of rules is not sufficient to represent all possible inferences in natural language, but it may take care of most of those that follow from considerations of form alone (i.e. are *formally* logical).

We are assuming that all propositions or sentences can be expressed in canonical form e.g. Aab, where A is an operator, representing a verb or connective, and a and b are classes or could be individual names α or β. We need now to know what types of operator can occur and what types of classes and individuals can occur.

Our first form is:

$$Nab \qquad \qquad \dots (1)$$

which shows the relation of class inclusion. Nab means "$a \subset b$" so the transitivity of the relations

$$(Nab \, . \, Nbc) \rightarrow (Nac)$$

represents the syllogism, although we must recall that some arguments depend on this transitivity and yet are not syllogistic; this applies, for example, to those that are classified as 'atomic relational'. The rules of the syllogism, in effect, test for this transitivity relationship.

Our second form is

$$Mxa \qquad \ldots (2)$$

where x is an individual name, and (2) represents class membership.

We next have

$$Rxy \qquad \ldots (3)$$

where we call the operator R a *relator*, e.g. ". . . is to the left of – – –", ". . . is taller than – – –", "above", "below", etc, are further examples.

Form (4) is

$$Rab \qquad \ldots (4)$$

which relates classes rather than individuals, and where Rab *can* be reduced, in part, to a class membership form, since "Welsh people are taller than Hindus" can be rewritten as Welsh belong to class a, Hindus to class b, and $a > b$. This we have already met with, our previous example involving Irishmen, Portuguese and Italians.

Arguments such as the above raise the point of cardinals associated with classes, and it also raises the matter of inequalities. We then see that it is necessary to retain a separate form such as (4) because of $a > b$ being a necessary part of the statement; this is much what we meant by the additional semantic rule mentioned before. The argument also presupposes that the shortest Irishman is still taller than the tallest Portuguese.

The notion of number, etc, can clearly be developed from (4), for example, if we have a set of classes a, b, . . ., n then we have a whole set of rules such as:

$$a = a$$
$$a = b \rightarrow b = a$$
$$a = b . b = c \rightarrow a = c$$
$$(a+b)c = c(a+b)$$
$$o+a = a+o$$
etc

where the cardinals associated with each class are the numbers, from which we can build an *integral domain*. We shall not of course pursue this matter further here. It is clear that we can reproduce much of mathematics within the domain of the calculus of classes and the calculus of relations, but we do not wish to do so, since mathematics can be reproduced as needed in practice from "shallower" bases.

3   The Computer Context of Logical Inference

An inference will be expected of the computer if, when being asked a question, it does not find the answer in the form of a ready made statement, or has not got the data which can be described by such a statement. This requires logical inference; we are at the moment thinking mainly of such inferences as being formal, but *non-formal* arguments may be logical but their logic depends on meaning and they are, in our categorization, either molecular or mixed arguments. They are also reducible to formal arguments if we set up the necessary formats and rules.

If, for example, the question is (?)Mxb = "Is x a b?" then the search is for Mxb. If you find, say, Myb and Axy, then you may have a basis for asserting something about Mxb. The first search is to pair off with the original terms, the second is for statements with one term (class or individual name) in common with the original statement, and this, suggests a further search for statements with terms in common with these, even though having nothing directly in common with the original, e.g. in the above example Myc could become relevant through Myb. This is precisely the relevance criteria which we discussed in the last chapter.

Problems of relevance also occur in *non-formal* inference. For example, let us suppose the following interpretation of our statements:

$$Mxb = \text{"Pat is Irish"} \qquad \dots (5)$$

$$Myb = \text{"Sean is Irish"} \qquad \dots (6)$$

$$Axy = \text{"Pat and Sean are brothers"} \qquad \dots (7)$$

$$Myc = \text{"Sean lives in Dublin"} \qquad \dots (8)$$

(6) and (7) clearly allow the inference "Pat is Irish", and this is

possible only by virtue of knowing what "being brothers" means. How then do we deal with this on a computer? The answer appears to be that we need to know the entailments of Relators, so for example:

x is taller than y→x's height >y's height, etc.

This problem arises all the time within the framework of factual theories, so we have an example such as:

"As a bar of metal cools, so it contracts" Therefore "A bar of metal is cooling" implies "The bar of metal is contracting". We write this last statement formally as Mzd, where z is the name of the bar of metal and d is the class of cooling objects. The statement which links Mzd with Mze, i.e. "this bar of metal is contracting" is the general one.

$$Mxd \rightarrow Mxe \qquad \ldots (9)$$

and also in this case

$$Mxe \rightarrow Mxd \qquad \ldots (10)$$

or

$$Mxe \leftarrow Mxd \qquad \ldots (11)$$

The extra statements which are needed to make the necessary inferences are rules of language (e.g. the use (meaning) of the word 'brother') or scientific hypotheses (hopefully, a mirror of the nature of reality); they are rules of entailment or, in a sense, semantic rules. It is these general rules that allow inference making *other than* on the grounds of logical *form* alone.

There are still problems however, since we really need quantifiers in statements (9), (10) and (11). However, the use of a combinatorial language can if necessary avoid their use. The inferences themselves can be derived in ordinary language, but this implies the need for a Thesaurus and a dictionary, as well as rules such as occur in language translation, for contextual definition, colloquialisms, etc. This can be supplied if the computer is to be able to accept ordinary English and identify synonymous forms in sentences or phrases.

Let us now look at (8), which was our statement of "second degree of relevance". Given the question Mxb, (8) alone supplies no relevant evidence. If we know (6) and (7), the implication is, as we have already agreed, clearcut. But if we have the following:

Mas = "Dublin is in Eire"

Sxy = "Pat and Sean live in the same town"

then we can infer that "Pat lives in Eire" and given the further proposition that "all people living in Eire are Irish" (i.e. Nrs, say) then again the conclusion is reached. Here we see clearly the need for some form of impression, ideally measured as precisely as in probability theory. We should write Nrs as Nrs(p) where p is the probability of the truth of Nrs. We are now at the point where we can use *modal operators*, and as a first approximation we can divide the interval (0, 1) in the following way:

$$(0) \quad \underset{1/18}{A} \underset{—\,7/18\,—}{B} \underset{2/18}{C_{(\frac{1}{2})}} \underset{—\,7/18\,—}{D} \underset{1/18}{E} \quad (1)$$

the end points 0 and 1 are

> 'certainly' (C)
> and
> 'certainly not' (N)

the intervals, A, B, C, D and E can be called

> "almost certainly not" (A)
> "probably not" (B)
> "may be" or "possibly" (C)
> "probably" (D)
> "almost certainly" (E)

This can be used easily enough where we have a measure such as a count of related events (Chapter 6). Where we have not such a definite measure, the problem is more difficult. We can show an example. First of all the question:

> "Is Jack the husband of Jill?"   ... (12)

If we have the appropriate marriage licence, etc., then we usually say 'certainly', even though obviously we could still be wrong. If though we do not know, then consider the following statements:

> "Jack lives with Jill"   ... (13)
> "Jack and Jill have the same surname"   ... (14)
> "Jack and Jill have different surnames"   ... (15)
> "Jack loves Jill"   ... (16)

"Jack is (almost) always with Jill"   ... (17)

"Jack does not know Jill"   ... (18)

"Jack has met Jill once"   ... (19)

Now given the truth of (13), (14), (16) and (17) then $\vdash$ A (12), where $\vdash$ means "is an accepted statement".

$$\text{If } \vdash (15), (16) \text{ then } \vdash C (12)$$

$$\text{If } \vdash (18) \text{ then } \vdash E (12)$$

$$\text{If } \vdash (19) \text{ then } \vdash B (12)$$

$$\text{If } \vdash (16), (17) \text{ then } \vdash D (12)$$

It is easy to see how this form of argument can be extended but we shall not attempt to carry out such extensions here.

We should notice that in the previous example the premises are presumed to have probability (p) = 1, but the argument is much the same if the premises have p $\langle 1$, since these will in turn be based on other premises whether explicitly stated or not. This is something which we presuppose in inference-making, though we must be aware of the dangers that attend such presuppositions.

We can in any case designate precise methods for providing probabilities in some cases and not in others. Whenever there is no precise measure, we tend to employ *heuristics*. These heuristics attempt to provide a plausible solution which can be reinforced by testing. The goal strength and the risk entailed in achieving the goal will, among other factors, increasingly influence the human decision taken as the uncertainty increases.

Kaplan and Schott [1], George [2], and others have tried to develop logics of uncertain inference which represents much of the actual inference making used by human beings. The problem for the computer is to manufacture starting heuristics which allow testing and adaptation and which are, where action is involved, of the "fail safe" variety. This argument connects deduction with our earlier discussion of induction (Chapter 6), and with the notion of minimum risk.

[1] A. Kaplan and D. Schott, *A Calculus for Empirical Classes*, Methodos, *3*. pp. 165–90, 1951.
[2] F. H. George, *The Brain as a Computer*, Pergamon Press, Oxford, 1961.

4 Models and Empirical Systems

It goes without saying that empirical systems represent bases for argument. Mathematics we need not further consider, but we must consider the cases such as arise in such empirical sciences as Chemistry, where we may be provided with the left hand side of a chemical formula and can then, if we know the chemical facts, supply the right hand side; this is, in essence, a semantic problem which presupposes the relevant knowledge.

This sort of scientific model can be extended indefinitely to cover any empirical information. We can use similar methods to describe definitional models such as are involved in a (1, 1) correspondence or other "geographical" or "geometrical" models which allow inference making in the same manner as is possible in, say, two-dimensional Euclidean Geometry, or as is implied in simple cases of class relationship by Euler-Venn diagrams. We shall say quite generally that all these arguments fall into two classes. The first is that of molecular arguments, where the necessity springs from the axioms of the empirical theory. The second class is that of relationships such as are implied by such things as isomorphisms, etc, which are a basis for valid argument by virtue of their form; this second class is really an extension of non-relational atomic arguments.

The computer thus needs a Thesaurus, a set of statements and rules of meaning (Semantic rules) which include all the axioms of an empirical science as well as the logical and syntactical rules of appropriate forms. It may also need to develop the Functional Calculi as a part of Recursive function theory but this is not needed as a basis for the use of mathematics in the problem of synthesis; it must however ultimately be relevant to simulation, and must be capable of being arrived at—as it has by humans—through heuristic generation.

The need for a Thesaurus will become clearer in the next chapter where we discuss natural language computing.[1] Here though let it be said that with any system of language that allows overlap of *meaning* or of synonymity, which is "complete" (or sufficient) overlap in a particular context, allows the interchange of words or phrases. This is essential to definitions where we wish to introduce new terms by reference to existing terms, either with shorthand purposes or to make some more refined distinction.

[1] F. H. George, The Development of Semantics Machines, *Cybernetics*, 1967, No. 3, pp. 145–172.

The problem of definitions which are normally verbal is a reminder that such definitions are achieved sometimes by pointing at things, events, pictures, etc (ostension). Here we have a basic problem for artificially intelligent systems. The human being does not argue or learn from words alone, but has "on line" senses (ears, eyes, etc) which allow of a sampling of the environment which confirms or infirms hypotheses (heuristics) and allows *understanding* whether made explicit in language or not.

Inference making is probably less concerned with formal relationships, than it is with semantics (or meaning) and this occurs for human beings in the context of behaviour (pragmatics). Human beings though obviously communicate by gesture, inflection, etc, as well as through language and this loss of information is difficult to replace in any computer simulation. We must think then of an ordinary digital computer by comparison as a "blind, half-deaf, etc" man who only *hears language*; he learns about his environment entirely by description. We shall now return to that highly abstracted system, the Calculus of Relations. This is clearly a fundamental logical system for computer use.[1]

5 The Calculus of Relations

A relation is something that exists between two or more of a set of individuals or between classes, or between individuals and classes. In mathematics we can talk of ordered pairs of numbers and, for example, we can define the class of all ordered pairs (x, y) such that the relation R holds between all x and y.

Similarly a function can be regarded as a relation R, say, such that Rxy, for each x and at most one y, where y is the value of the function for argument x. More generally, we can talk of ordered n-tuples of numbers and functions of n variables. This permits the derivation of the whole of classical mathematics, when we assume a suitable domain and an axiomatic foundation for arithmetic. Recursive functions are the ultimate expression of this generalized mathematics, but we can develop all of intuitionistic mathematics by a calculus involving constants alone.

1 F. H. George, Simple Adaptive programs for Computers. A paper read, by invitation of the U.S. Department of Health at the Conference of Cybernetics held at the University of California, Los Angeles, 1962.

Following Maron and Levien[1] we can represent dyadic relations
by diagrams such as in Figure 1.

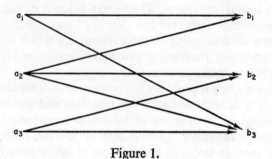

Figure 1.

Which represents the set of relations

$$Ra_1b_1$$
$$Ra_2b_2$$
$$Ra_1b_3$$
$$Ra_2b_1$$
$$Ra_2b_3$$
$$Ra_3b_2$$
$$Ra_3b_3$$

This could also be represented as a matrix:

R	b_1	b_2	b_3
a_1	1	1	1
a_2	1	0	1
a_3	0	1	1

We can now think of our calculus as a Structure Matrix[1] and the
overall relation to neural nets becomes clear cut. The function matrix
is then a measure of the probable relation, so that

$$Ra_1b_1 \rightarrow Ra_1b_1(p) \rightarrow Ra_1b_1(\tfrac{1}{3}), \text{ say}$$

So for an arbitrary set of probabilities the function Matrix may read:

[1] M. E. Maron and G. Levien, The relational data file, Rand Memo, 1966.

R	b_1	b_2	b_3
a_1	$\frac{1}{3}$	$\frac{1}{3}$	$\frac{1}{3}$
a_2	$1/10$	0	$9/10$
a_3	0	$\frac{3}{4}$	$\frac{1}{4}$

We can now derive more complex relationships such as the *relative product* $(R|R)$.

$$R^2 = R|R = \text{"} \ldots \text{ is an R of an R of } \ldots \text{"}$$

$$R|S = \text{"} \ldots \text{ is an R of an S of } \ldots \text{"}$$

i.e. $$R^2 ab = Ra \subset R \subset b$$

i.e.   If R is "a son of" then

$$R^2 ab \to a \text{ is a son of a son of } b$$

$$= a \text{ is a grandson of } b.$$

We can have the inverse R^{-1} of R which is such that $RR^{-1} = I$

$$\text{So } R|R^{-1} = R^0 = \text{identification} = I$$

We can, of course, generalize these notions, so we get

$$R^{-2} \equiv R^{-1}|R^{-1} \equiv (R^{-1})^2 \equiv (R^2)^{-1} \qquad \ldots (9)$$

and in general

$$R^m = R^n|R^p \text{ where } m = n+p$$

The usual rules of symmetry, transitivity and reflexivity hold for some relations and not others and so we can go on and describe our calculus in increasing detail; we shall not attempt to do so here.

We can develop a powerful formal language which can then be mapped on to the theory of probability, giving us an "empirical" calculus of relations suitable for descriptive purposes in conditions of uncertainty, provided we can deal with the problem of Semantics.

6 Inference Making in the "Real World"

We, as human beings, use ordinary language to communicate our ideas, concepts and thoughts. We argue in ordinary language and to do so we use formal logic and also a knowledge of empirical facts.

We can say on one hand "three miles and four more miles make seven miles in all" and this is formally true since $3 + 4 = 7$, but also factually true since we can observe it to be so. However, all items are not additive in this way, and there are in any case other relations between features of the empirical world which allow us to derive valid arguments. The fact, for example, that we have ten boxes and only nine items to go in them, allows us to infer that at least one box will remain empty at any moment.

Whether or not we seek to support our formal logics by semantic rules[1] or a further set of empirical axioms,[2] we must support them somehow, sometimes by adding to the formal rules and thus in effect making a semantic matter into a syntactic one. We must somehow embody empirical descriptions if we are to be able to use empirical argument. Evidence for believing some empirical statement, or statements, must thus come from other empirical statements, whose relevance can only be understood by some form of semantic (or syntactic) rules. We now need to repeat a little of what has been said on *connotation* and *denotation*.

The connotation and denotation[3] of statements must be known, and the denotation of words. The connotation of a statement blank like " $---$ is a brother of . . . " (B_1) is the set of all meaningful statements that can be composed by substituting proper names into the blanks. We must also know the *entailments* of the phrase and this is the set of statement blanks that can be filled up to make the connotation. Furthermore the categorizing of relational phrases into symmetries, etc, is a first step towards discoveries of these entailments. Let us take up an example of an entailment more closely, where $B_1 \equiv \ldots$ is the brother of $---$, we must say B_1xy entails the following:

> "x and y have the same parents"   . . . (10)

> "x and y have the same nationality"   . . . (11)
>   (judged by parents)

> and
> we may also add the probabilistic statements

> "x and y have the same name"   . . . (12)

[1] W. Pitts and W. S. McCulloch, A logical calculus of the ideas immanent in nervous activity, *Bull, Math, Biophys.* 1943.

[2] B. Raphael, SIR: a computer program for semantic information retrieval, 1964, Fall Joint Comp Conf., 25.

[3] F. H. George, The development of semantic machines, *Cybernetics*, 1967, pp. 145–72.

"x and y were brought up by the same people"   ... (13)

"x and y look something alike"   ... (14)
etc.

In fact going from (12) to (14) is probably going in the direction of decreasing probability. However, these logical entailments are really a part of the definition of and the intension of B_1. Then other features may be shown to follow from these, either formally or factually.

Logic Theorem Proving

We shall now look briefly at the related field of logic theorem proving.[1] This entails showing that a well formed formula is, or is not, a theorem of some calculus, such as the Propositional Calculus. Because the interest is in heuristic methods, it goes without saying that an algorithm can not be used. This leads to something like a simulation of human theorem-proving.

Newell, Shaw and Simon follow various methods of seeking a proof. The first is that of *substitution*. This is the well known method of starting from a known theorem and by legitimate substitutions trying to derive the statement needing proof. The second method is called *detachment*. Given that a subproblem may be solved and given that this subproblem implies the main problem, then of course the main problem is solved. So if A can be proved and if A implies B, B is proved. The *chaining* method is similar and makes use of the transitivity of the implication relation. These methods can all be used after the structure of the formula to be proved has been identified.

Such methods as those mentioned above, clearly do not guarantee success, but they will sometimes—as they do with humans—prove successful. There is no suggestion in this work as yet, that permits of the derivation of new methods. Such a step, which is perfectly possible in principle, demands a more complex system, and one which

[1] A. Newell, J. C. Shaw and H. A. Simon, The theorem proving machine. In *Computers and Thought* (E. Feigenbaum and J. Feldman, eds.), New York: McGraw Hill, 1963.

H. Wang, Proving theorems by pattern recognition. I Comm. Assoc. Mach., 1960, *3*, 220–34.

is also adaptive. Indeed this further generation of generators is, of course, a problem primarily of induction.

From the point of view of this monograph, the importance of logic theorem proving lies as much with the ability to derive the correct result, as with the methods used. For us therefore, an algorithm's use is perfectly acceptable.

The main point here is that in this chapter, prior to this section, we had premises which permitted the derivation of conclusions. We now add methods for saying that a particular statement is a theorem (i.e. true) in the system. Such methods form an essential appendage to our logical apparatus.

8

Language

1 Language as vital to Intelligence

It has already been argued that language performs a vital role in cognitive activity, and to understand human thinking certainly implies the need to understand linguistic usage. This is a very large undertaking and we must remind ourselves again that our more specific search is for realistic starting conditions for modelling purposes. If the modelling process—here the computer program—is self-correcting, we have an evolutionary process taking place that will, we hope, ultimately lead us to a realistic model of human linguistic usage. These matters have been the source of exhaustive discussions by psychologists, philosophers and the like.[1] Much of language is concerned with the answering of questions and always involves data retrieved. Inference making is both a source of asking questions, and a means of answering them, as was made clear in the last chapter in the example of Pat and Sean. Let us look first at data retrieval.

Data retrieval implies a search, and search procedures can be either algorithmic or heuristic. There are many forms of computer storage, such as in list-processing which are essentially treelike. Sometimes whole branches of the tree can be omitted from the

---

[1] A. Naess, Towards a theory of interpretation and preciseness, *Semantics and the Philosophy of Language*, L. Linsky (ed.), Univ. of Illinois Press, 1952; R. Carnap, Empiricism, Semantics and Ontology, *Semantics and the Philosophy of Language*, L. Linsky (ed.), Univ of Illinois Press, 1952; A. Korzybski, *Science and Sanity*, Lancaster, Pa., 1933; F. H. George, Pragmatics, *J. Phil. Phen. Res.*, 1956, 226–35.

search, or the search can in some other way be "short-circuited"; this entails the use of heuristics.

We can think of natural language computing in several different ways. We can think of what is now considered traditional language translation, with an input in one language and an output in another language. But this is not our main interest; for we are mainly concerned here with using a language like English in something of the role of a compiler language. Our language should be like *PL1*, *Cobol*, *Fortran* or *Algol*, in that it is compiler, but it is not primarily intended to program a computer in the ordinary sense, but to allow self-programming to occur. This should happen in much the same way that ordinary language changes, in a conversation, the attitude or the "disposition to respond"[1] in the listener.

2 Language Translation

A more detailed look at the problem of language translation[2] is now called for.

Our computer store contains a dictionary, a thesaurus and set of syntactical rules, and we must code our languages into machine code. Thus if A = 01, L = 12, E = 05, then the string (01, 12, 05) = ALE. Thus if (1,1) correspondence existed between words in the two languages, translation would be extremely simple. The very fact that words have different meanings (e.g. pen, kid) and verbs have different tenses, and further, that the context of the whole phrase, sentence or paragraph conveys a specific meaning to particular words, making such words *context sensitive*, makes in turn such a word-by-word translation ultimately unfeasible. We shall discuss this again later, but even in the immediate problem of language translation the difficulty exists.

One way of dealing with our difficulty over verbs is to take, for example, the stem of a verb such as 'to decide' and add different endings making 'decides', 'decided', etc.

One method of dealing with this problem of ambiguity is to have

---

[1] C. W. Morris, *Signs, Language and Behaviour*, New York, Prentice Hall, 1946.

[2] A. D. Booth and W. N. Locke, *Machine Translation of Languages*, New York: Wiley, 1955; D. Y. Panov, *Automatic Translation*, Oxford: Pergamon Press, 1960; H. P. Edmundson (ed.), *Proceedings of the National Symposium on Machine Translation*, Harvard Univ. Press, 1960.

what we call a structure number (SN2) which gives a key to the subject matter, or context, so that if the subject is that of birds especially associated with water (SN246, say) then 'pen' is given one meaning, but if the discussion is of writing equipment (SN218) the word 'pen' is given another meaning. A method can be derived which allows the computer to *learn* the most likely structure number by a check on the words and without as yet attempting translation. (SN1) is used as a first structure number to identify parts of speech as we show in the following table:

Part of Speech	SN1
Noun	1
Pronoun	2
Adjective	3
Adverb	4
Verb	5
Preposition	6
Conjunction	7
Interjection	8

Thus putting the two code numbers together, we have for example, in French, the words 'ancien régime' which will be coded 'ancien' (SN13) and 'régime' (SN11). Syntactical rules must, of course, be known in some measure so that generally it is known to the computer that, in French, adjectives come *after* the related nouns, and in English it is the other way around; the above example is thus an exception to the general rule, and must be noted as such. We really need to have a key to the number of standard sentence structures[1] and identify the sentence structure, SN1 and SN2, and then we are in a position to translate on a word-by-word basis with a better chance of success. The store usually has its glossaries listed alphabetically, but it has been suggested by Sarkar[2] that a better method is to keep count of the frequency of occurrences of the words and keep the most frequent at the top of lists which are divided according to their structure numbers or according to such classification. This is essentially an adaptive procedure.

Finally, a third structure number (SN3) deals with idiomatic expressions, so that the context of the recognized idiom changes the

[1] N. Chomsky, *Syntactic Structures*, Mouton, 1957.
[2] P. A. Sarkar, *Artificial intelligence and natural language*, Ph.D. Thesis, Bristol, 1967.

translation. For example, "tell it to the Marines" has a purely idiomatic meaning which should have an SN3 number informing the computer that it is, in fact, idiomatic.

We must next consider how many of the difficulties of machine translation apply to natural language computing. The answer is that they all apply if ordinary English or French is to be used, but we do not need to have a glossary of quite the same kind, since we are now concerned with the computer *understanding*, in the sense that the computer may have to do something by way of an output, or change its internal state, or both. The computer must now tackle the problem of *meaning* more fully and must be able to modify its program as a result of statements made to it. Nevertheless, the problems of traditional language translation and artificial intelligence with natural language are in many ways very similar. We will now consider some of the difficulties encountered in natural language computing.

3 Flexibility and Definition

In the computer, we are dealing, as we have already made clear, with what is essentially a "blind man", whose only sense is that of hearing language, and this we see as a great deficiency when we come to the application of such computing in the cause of simulating human behaviour.

"On line" processes are needed to create new situations, allow search and direct sampling of the environment. These are matters which we, as human beings, would recognize directly with our senses. The "off line" computer must recognize this same data from its data tape alone. This is a reminder of the difficulties encountered by attempting to program a computer which is not in possession of eyes or ears or other methods for acquiring direct patterns, or their machine equivalent.

The advantages of analogy, or the recognition of similarities springs for humans from the visual sense, and we must, it seems, supply some equivalent if we are to hope for equivalent results. Nevertheless, there is the possibility of the use of analogy within the existing conventional computer system with additional linguistic facilities. If A→B, (where → means "causally implies") then if B→C, then we could argue for an obvious similarity between A→B and B→C, which seems to suggest the conclusion A→C (A "causally implies" C).

Similarly, if $a_1 \rightarrow b_1$, $a_2 \rightarrow b_2$, where $(a_1, a_2) \in A$ and $(b_1, b_2) \in B$, then a different sort of similarity is implied; a similarity which could be basic to making an inductive inference.

In ordinary language, we might think of "definition by analogy", and say "adding is like subtracting, but the opposite", "football is like cricket, but involves bats and balls rather than balls alone". This last example brings out the important point that a computer must be able to rearrange its program to meet new circumstances, and the rearrangement may occur in putting together familiar sub-routines, perhaps adding one or more which is new, or even modifying one or more instructions within an existing subroutine. So if X is like Y, where Y is a sub-routine, then try Y, and then modify it to make it slightly different. The mode of making it different, the mode of variation is not trial-and-error, since the likeness, if correct, must suggest a mode of variation which is selective. This is surely a type of "insight learning". Let us now look at a more specific type of definining.

Given a linguistic system which describes, or is capable of describing, a certain process, we are faced with many problems of how such a language can be extended:

       1 by adding labels
       2 by using detailed definitions.

Let us illustrate the problem by an example.

We have a *linguistic* program which describes data which is placed in store. Let us call the elements, data items and label them a_1, a_2, ..., a_n and we can have varying amounts of these items. They can also be categorized in a number of ways, placed in different configurations according to structure numbers, classes, etc. It is, of course, to be made clear that this data in store is supposed to reflect an actual external state of affairs. The actual state could refer to pieces in games like checkers or chess, or items stored in a warehouse. All that matters to us here is how we describe them, and how we generalize this language of description.

Let us start by considering *questions* only where all questions *start with* some interrogative word, and the question is put to the computer.

We shall now assume our vocabulary contains at least the following words:

1 How
2 Why
3 When
4 Where
5 Who
6 What
7 Which

and discuss their implications for computer questioning, Restricted to the above seven interrogative starting words, we shall have to develop (at least) seven procedures.

Let us look at a simple "starting flow chart":

The use of a simple shift operation and a comparison with a "template" (fixed word in a register) is enough to make the distinctions of Figure 1.

We now wish to look at the procedures, and we look at 'how' the procedure, as an example. By the use of 'how', we shall take the questioner to mean that he wishes for a description of some set of causal relations; it is, if you like, the field of *explanation*. Look at some examples:

1 [How] do you [know] [Charles] [lives] in [Dartmouth]?
2 [How] do you [mend] a [puncture]?
3 [How] do you [mend] a [bicycle puncture], where the bicycle has [heavy tyres]?
4 [How] can I [climb] [Mount Everest]?
5 [How] [much] can I [save] by [not drinking]?
6 [How] [many] soldiers [are] there in your [regiment]?
and so on.

No one procedure is likely to be easily derived that is to prove wholly acceptable for 'how'. In this respect their problem is much like that of formalizing a word or a term, which entails the process of removing all ambiguity. Such a process is always carried out at the expense of the full range of everyday meaning. We must also look at certain *key features* of any sentence before we can finally decide on any starting procedure.

The key features in the above examples are placed in square brackets. The basic key is 'how' itself, and this must, of course, occur in the sentence to introduce any how-procedure. 'How' is not, in fact, necessarily the first word in the sentence, so we can have:

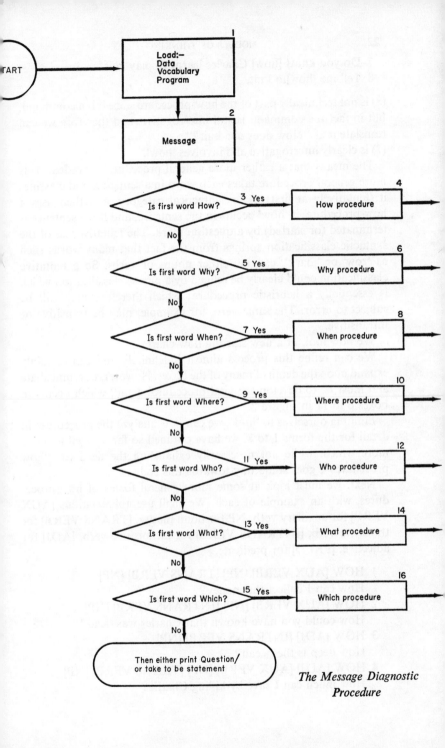

The Message Diagnostic
Procedure

7 Do you know [how] Charles learnt to play golf?
8 Tell me [how]to knit.

(8) is not technically part of the how-procedure since it is a command, but in fact the command is still interrogative, and therefore we can translate it as "How does one knit?"
(7) is clearly interrogative and involves 'how'.

The means that a rather more general procedure is needed. This more general procedure takes each word in a sentence, and classifies it (tentatively at first) as to syntactical category, and then uses a how-procedure, if 'how' occurs in the sentence, and if the sentence is terminated (or started) by a question mark. The tentativeness of the syntactic classification springs from the fact that many words such as 'row' or 'mark', can be, either nouns or verbs. So a tentative classification could clearly be refined by a phrase classification which is essentially a heuristic procedure; which therefore may still be subject to error. The same verb, for example, may be transitive or intransitive.

We now look at a new starting flow chart.

We can refine this process almost indefinitely and can certainly expand upon the detail of many of the boxes. However, our immediate aim must be to develop the vital procedural detail, which occurs in boxes 6 to 11 in Figure 2.

Limiting ourselves to 'how', we can now analyze the procedures in detail for the forms 1 to 8, we have outlined so far, as well as some more which, while not necessarily exhausting the need for "how procedures", goes some way towards this end.

Next, we must look at some more general forms of how-procedures, with an example of each. We shall use abbreviations [AUX VERB] for auxiliary verb, NP for noun phrase, [TRANS VERB] for transitive verb, [INTRANS VERB] for intransitive verb, [ADJ] for adjective, [PRED] for predicate.

1 HOW [AUX VERB] [NP] [TRANS VERB] [NP]
   How can I collect the money?
2 HOW [AUX VERB] [NP] [INTRANS VERB] [NP]
   How could you have known that Charles was dead?
3 HOW [ADJ] [INTRANS VERB] [NP]
   How deep is the ocean?
4 HOW [ADJ] [AUX VERB] [NP] [TRANS VERB] [NP]
   How much can I save by killing Charlie?

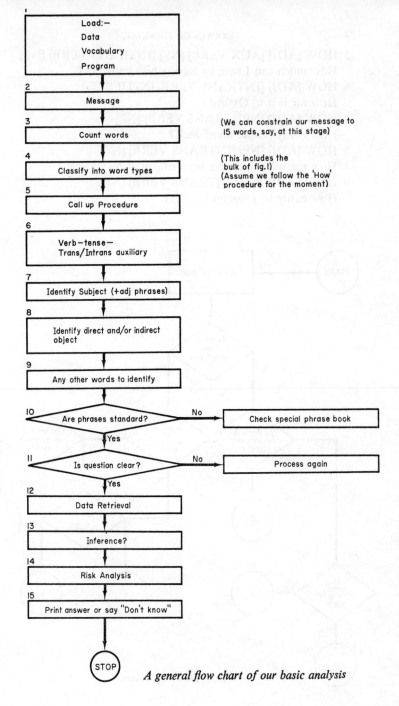

START

1. Load:—
   Data
   Vocabulary
   Program

2. Message

3. Count words

   (We can constrain our message to 15 words, say, at this stage)

4. Classify into word types

   (This includes the bulk of fig.1)
   (Assume we follow the 'How' procedure for the moment)

5. Call up Procedure

6. Verb—tense—
   Trans/Intrans auxiliary

7. Identify Subject (+adj phrases)

8. Identify direct and/or indirect object

9. Any other words to identify

10. Are phrases standard? — No → Check special phrase book

    ↓ Yes

11. Is question clear? — No → Process again

    ↓ Yes

12. Data Retrieval

13. Inference?

14. Risk Analysis

15. Print answer or say "Don't know"

STOP

A general flow chart of our basic analysis

5 HOW [ADJ] [AUX VERB] [NP] [INTRANS VERB] [NP]
   How much can I save by having him know me?
6 HOW [ADJ] [INTRANS VERB] [NP] [PRED]
   How far is it to Oxford?
7 HOW [ADJ] [NP] [TRANS VERB] [NP]
   How many people loved Jack?
8 HOW [ADJ] [NP] [INTRANS VERB] [NP]
   How many people have been smiled at by Charlie?
9 HOW [ADV P] [NP] [TRANS VERB] [NP]
   How easily he rows on the river.

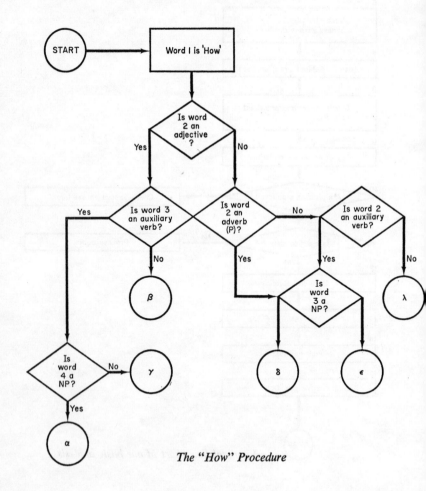

The "How" Procedure

10 HOW [ADV P] [NP] [INTRANS VERB] [NP]
    How calmly he allows people to hug him.

This is not necessarily a complete list but it will be sufficient for
our analytic purpose. Figure 3 shows a flow chart for this set, which
still excludes the use of the word 'how', other than in the first
position.

We now carry out our check procedure. Let us take an example:
How many people live in Swansea?

'How' and ? are associated, and this clearly implies a how-
procedure; 'many' is identified as an adjective, so we have:

	[NP]
[How ADJ]	[AUX VERB]
	[INTRANS VERB]

'people' at W3 implies NP, so we look for:

	[TRANS VERB]
[NP]	[INTRANS VERB]

The verb is transitive, since 'live in' is used here transitively.
'Swansea' is the final noun (NP) so we have type 9.

The process for the input part of the "how-procedure" is now
clear and we can proceed to outline the other interrogative procedures
rather more briefly, by merely providing in Figures 4 and 5, the broad
issues involved in the procedures. Before we do this, however, it
would be as well to outline the result of identification of the appropriate procedure. Granted we have a how-procedure, the computer
merely needs to know what the key terms are. For example, if it is
of type 1, then it is important for the computer to know what to do
(e.g. *collect* something) and then what is to be collected and in our
example it was *money* and finally who or what is to do the collecting
and it turns out to be *I*. We say in effect "How (do) I collect (the)
money?". This involves data retrieval, and we proceed now to search
our data store for information on money, money-collection and
perhaps we need to know *where from*. So the first output may be:

"Who/what are you collecting money for?" and then we add
another key phrase to the sentence which now reads:

'How (do) I collect (the) money for the Spastic Society in
Birmingham?'.

The detail can be refined as necessary, and the degree of refining

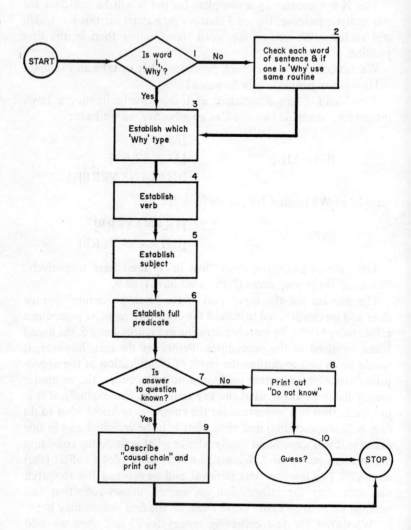

The "Why" Procedure

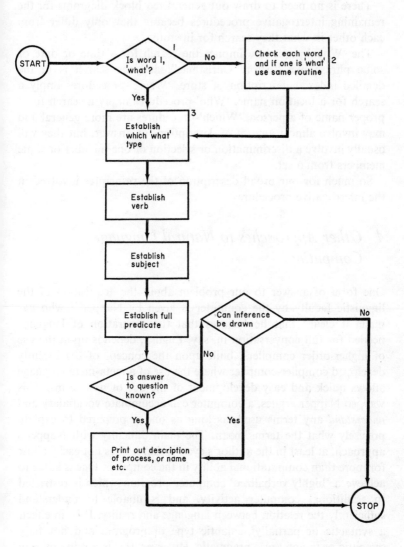

The "What" Procedure

depends on the stored information and the suggested degree of precision implied by the question.

There is no need to draw out generalized block diagrams for the remaining interrogative procedures because they only differ from each other in what they search for in store.

The 'When'-procedure implies the search for a time or date or some phrase like "before Christmas", and the search is in the detailed indexed description of store. 'Where'-procedures imply a search for a location name. 'Who'-procedures imply a search for a proper name of a person. 'Which'-procedures are more general and may involve almost any set of descriptions in answer, but they will usually involve a discrimination or selection of one member or some members from a set.

So much for our broad description of the principles involved in the interrogative procedures.

4   Other Approaches to Natural Language Computing

One form of answer to our problem about the acquisition of the linguistic faculty by the computer is given by Napper[1] who has made it clear[2] that he believes that the generation of language needed for full conversation in, say, English, depends upon the use of higher-order compilers, built upon the concept of the recently developed compiler-compiler where the use of a meta-meta language allows quick and easy development of the use of new terms. This way, so Napper argues, a computer can accumulate vocabulary and *understand* any terms used, as long as one is prepared to explain precisely what the terms mean. The main difficulty with Napper's approach, at least in the author's eyes, is that it does not easily allow for more than computational ability in the computer. One is liable to achieve a 'highly verbalized' computer program which is restricted to traditional computer activity, and is unable to understand sufficiently the relation between language and reality. It is, in effect, a syntactic or partially semantic type of program and not fully semantic or in any sense pragmatic. However, this is not in any way

[1] R. B. E. Napper, *A system of programming in natural English*, Ph.D. Thesis, Manchester, 1964.
[2] Personal communication

to deny the usefulness of Napper's work; it suggests, though, that it has a slightly different aim from ours.

There are a number of other efforts which have been made in the direction of natural language computing and we should mention at least the following:

5 Baseball

Baseball[1] is a language designed to answer questions of a factual kind.

If asked where the Boston Red Sox played baseball on July 7, 1961, then the program produced a specification list which uses the question to generate the details needed, e.g. Question: Where/Red Sox/Date/etc. A dictionary is used to generate the specification list, and the program determines whether a question has been asked, and if so, to supply the content of the question, which cues the answer. The data is contained in a hierarchical fashion in store, e.g.

Months

June—July—August

Place 1 Place 2, etc.

Day 1 Day 2, etc.

and so on.

The method used for Baseball, is essentially the same as that used by the author (George 1966, 1967)[2] although in Baseball there is no inference-making procedure.

6 Proto-Synthex and Synthex

Simmons[3] has produced a language called *Synthex* which involves the process of "word-indexing" a natural language text, and subse-

---

[1] B. E. Green, A. K. Wolf, C. Chomsky and K. Laughery, Baseball: an automatic question answerer. In *Computers and Thought*, E. A. Feigenbaum and J. Feldman (eds.), New York: McGraw Hill, 1963.

[2] F. H. George, Hypothesis Confirmation on a digital computer, *Symp. on Bionics*, Dayton, Ohio, 1966.

F. H. George, The development of semantic machines, *Cybernetics*, 1967, No. 3, pp. 145–72.

[3] W. R. F. Simmons, Answering English questions by computer: a survey. Communications of the A.C.M., 1962, *8*, 1, 53–70.

quently analysing its grammatical content. Synthex is the original name of the language called *Proto synthex*. The idea is to extract answers to questions where the information referred to is in the form of a text.

First of all we must consider the problem of syntactical analysis. Synthex talks of:

A sentence which is nominative or contains a noun phrase, modifiers and complements as well as verbs, or verb phrases, modifiers and complements. This is consistent with most syntactical analyses and becomes relevant as soon as we decode, or encode, information from or into ordinary English sentences.

A list of entries of key words is kept as derived from the text, so that given a question such as "How powerful is the shock of an electric eel?" we look up the key words (content words) such as 'shock' 'electric', etc. and here we clearly see the need for synonyms, since one of the content words is 'powerful' and this could equally well appear as 'strong' in a text.

We next look at the 'interaction' of these key content words, so that in effect we are searching for some such statement as "the shock that is given by an electric eel is in the vicinity of x volts" or some such answer to the question.

The process depends for its effectiveness on appropriate indexing, cross-indexing and scoring to extract the necessary information. So-called VAPS numbers (V = volume, A = article, P = paragraph and S = sentence) are used to index the text and frequency of occurrence is the basis of scoring.

When a suitable sentence, or set of sentences is extracted, a comparison is made, after parsing has taken place, with the original question. So that the question form "Is x a y" has an answer like "No, x is not a y", where the comparison of x with y and y with y is obvious. So-called dependency grammars are used for the parsing process.

7 Sad Sam

Lindsay[1] has developed a semantic analyzing machine (SAD SAM) for analyzing semantic relationships in family-tree form. He includes

1 R. K. Lindsay, Inferential memory as the basis of machines which understand natural language. In *Computers and Thought*, E. A. Feigenbaum and J. Feldman, (eds.), New York: McGraw Hill, 1963.

kinship relationships and phrase-structure grammatical analysis[1] and this again is similar to the process of Baseball and also the author's work.[2]

It is of interest that SAD SAM[3] appeals to the work of Osgood[4] and Mowrer[5] in its theory of language. Osgood's basic argument is that a word elicits associated internal responses which can be described on certain dimensions of good-bad, strong-weak, etc. The meaning of the combination of words making up a sentence is the mean of these values. Mowrer, on the other hand, talks of inter-conditioning between the first and subsequent parts of a sentence. These notions may need to be included at some stage but they are clearly insufficient as they stand, since "Jack killed Joe" would mean the same as "Joe killed Jack" for Osgood's theory, whereas apparently "Jack loves Jill" could equally well mean the same as "Jack hates Jill".

Fodor[6] has shown explicitly the difficulties which have been widely recognized to exist in the more narrowly behaviouristic theories of language.[7] Language does not conform to the stimulus-responses theories of learning in many respects. The idea that a word is regularly associated with the object it represents is too simple. We as human beings learn the meaning of words often without having any contact with the denotation of the word. This is because knowledge is acquired even more from description than from acquaintance. Thus it is that a mediating system is necessary. Indeed it is the map-making plan-forming type of behaviour which is characteristic of symbolization. This type of activity cannot be immediately explained in terms of stimuli and responses and calls for a more

[1] N. Chomsky, *Syntactic Structures*, Mouton, 1957.

[2] F. H. George, Hypothesis Confirmation on a digital computer, *Symp. on Bionics*, Dayton, Ohio, 1966.

[3] R. K. Lindsay, Inferential memory as the basis of machines which understand natural language. In *Computers and Thought*, E. A. Feigenbaum and J. Feldman (eds.), New York: McCraw Hill, 1963.

[4] C. E. Osgood and G. Suci, *The measurement of meaning*, University of Illinois Press, 1957.

[5] O. H. Mowrer, The psycholinguist looks at language, 1954, *American Psychologist*, 9 (10).

[6] A. J. Fodor, Could meaning be an I_m? *J. verb Learn. Verb. Behav.*, 1965, *4*, 73–81.

[7] See references on pages 115 and 129 especially. Although the work of Charles Morris (page 116) and C. K. Ogden and J. A. Richards, *The Meaning of Meaning*, Harcourt Brace, 1938. For a popular account of Semantics, see F. H. George, *Semantics*, English Universities Press.

sophisticated type of theory. This same argument we have said of course applies not only to language but to most other higher level cognition.

8 Sir

Raphael's[1] SIR is yet another language program which is again somewhat similar to those discussed already. He uses *word association* as a basic concept. He attempts to deal in semantic analysis, with inference making, but, no syntactical analysis. The most interesting additional feature that Raphael's program possesses is that of relevance, or relatedness. This problem of relevance is, as we have seen, fundamental to any language usage. Raphael uses a typical relation

$$Rxy$$

to be represented in SIR by attribute value pairs placed on property lists. The relationships are not normally symmetric since most statements, such as "everybody is a person" would be nonsense if thought of as symmetric. He achieves some considerable degree of flexibility by lists of properties which are associated with the values of attributes, e.g. the property-list associated with MAN would contain (SUBPART ((PLIST (NAME, FINGER)))). The sentence forms recognized by SIR then correspond to specific relations in a manner which is similar to those already discussed above.

We shall not carry this discussion of existing natural language programs any further, but we should note at this point similar work done by Maron and Levien[2] which is concerned more immediately with data retrieval and logic, Phillip's[3] question-answerer, Darlington[4] translation into symbolic logic which is again somewhat similar to the methods of the author, Bohnert's model,[5] Forster's interrogation language[6] and Colin's[7] practical example of a "conversational mode" program.

[1] B. Raphael, SIR: A computer program. By semantic information retrieval. *Fall Joint Comp. Conference*, 1964, 5, 25.

[2] M. E. Maron and G. Levien, The relational data file, 1966, *Rand Memo*.

[3] A. V. Phillips, A question answering routine. Memo 16, Artif. Intell. Proj., MIT, Cambridge, Mass., 1960.

[4] J. L. Darlington, A COMIT program for the Davis-Putnam algorithm, Res. Lab. Electron Mech. Transl. Grp., Cambridge, Mass.: MIT, 1964.

[5] H. G. Bohnert, An English-like extension of an applied predicate calculus, AFOSR-TN 62-3. I.B.M., Yorktown Heights, 1962.

[6] J. M. Forster, Interrogation languages. A paper read at Edinburgh, 1965.

[7] A. J. T. Colin, A simple program for us in the 'conversational mode', *The Computer Journal*, 9, 3, 238-41, 1966.

All these efforts have a number of features in common which are similar to the author's and therefore, in general, different from the approach of Napper. Some use inference-making as well as data retrieval and some use artificial language instead of natural, whether as an approximation to natural language or as an intermediate translation step to encourage the inference making process. The basic problem of *meaning* and the associated problems of *connotation*, *denotation*, *synonymity*, *analytic statements*, *synthetic statements*, *entailment*, etc, all arise, as do the problems of the distinction between syntax, semantics and pragmatics.[1] There is also the problem of truth, confirmation, factual support, etc, to be considered,[2] and the need to retain an internal model of sources of information as well as a model of oneself inside the computer.[3]

9 The Integrated Pattern

In Part I of this book an attempt was made to give a brief picture of cognition as viewed by psychologists and to a lesser extent philosophers, Definitions, sufficient for our purpose, were given of the principal cognitive terms. This in a sense was the interpretation for which models have been dealt with in Part II.

The models make no pretence at being complete since, as far as simulation is concerned, such features as emotions have been omitted. There seems though to be some hope that we have supplied models which can collectively simulate rational behaviour for many humanlike purposes, particularly at the level of human thought.

Let us talk of an automaton now as something which, as a set of computer programs, can reason and talk, can construct concepts and hypotheses, can play games and accept new information to change strategics and hypotheses where needed. In fact Decision Making in the form of using utilities, probabilities and then the various game playing strategies has received less attention than logical and linguistic ability. We remedy this defect in some small part in Part III, but a lot still remains to be done.

[1] R. Carnap, *Introduction to Semantics*, Cambridge, Mass., 1942.

[2] J. G. Kemeny and P. Oppenheim, Degree of factual support, *Philos. Sci.*, *19*, 307–24, 1952.

[3] M. Kochen, D. M. Mackay, M. E. Maron, M. Scriven and L. Uhr, *Computers and Comprehension*, Rand Memo. RM–4065–PR, 1964.

Against this we have automata capable of logical analysis far ahead of most human beings, a greater precision in linguistics, even if less flexible in using language; this is a matter of giving such automata experience.

This then is the scheme, to design an automaton to actively participate in an environment. It must be given enough ability to change its own skills as a function of its experience. Such an approach to thinking may be long term but there seem to be grounds for optimism if the method is sufficiently followed through, i.e. large scale integrated programs written which have large numbers of sub routines available, and which have the ability to adapt, even to the extent of changing the sub routines it uses.

PART THREE

TOWARDS AN INTEGRATED MODEL

This last part of the monograph is brief and simply tries to summarize and bring together what has been said in parts I and II.

It is tempting at this stage to take a piece of description of everyday behaviour:

'I was walking down the hill when I saw David, whom I recognized immediately in spite of the fact that it is nearly twenty years since we last met. He smiled and said ". . ." '

and show the equivalent flow charts in terms of recognition, speech, etc. The need to do this certainly exists, but the fact is that such an undertaking would be premature and far too large a business to be appropriate in this short monograph.

Since we are talking primarily of thinking, perhaps it would be wise at this point to distinguish different types of thinking and relate them to what we are trying to achieve.

Neisser has distinguished types of thinking as follows:

1 *Productive* and *blind* thinking. This really is the distinction between insight and trial-and-error and represents two stages of our model.

2 *Creative* and *constrained*. This is a difference of degree. The constrained is represented by limits on a solution or a clear cut goal. Creative is 'free thinking' implying absence of constraints.

3 *Intuition* and *reason*. We have said that these differ only by degree, if at all at the organic level. It is equivalent to Reichenbach's distinction between discovery and justification.

4 *Autistic* and *realistic* thinking. We have thought seriously only

of realistic thinking as opposed to an emotionally coloured process.

5 *Levels* of *consciousness*. We have made no attempt at this stage to seriously distinguish between levels of consciousness, but 3 above is directly relevant to this point. This same argument covers *primary* and *secondary* thought processes.

6 Finally, we have ourselves made the distinction between *sequential* and *multiple* processes.

There is little doubt that further distinctions could be made and should be made for certain purposes in certain contexts. This note merely reminds us of the complexity of the material we are dealing with.

9

In Summary

1 Summarizing

This book has been divided into three parts. The first part (Chapters 1 to 4) attempted to lay down a background to our methods, to define terms sufficiently for our purpose and make distinctions which seem necessary to get to grips with our model-making procedures, which followed in the second part of the book (Chapters 5 to 8 inclusive); part III summarizes.

Let us recapitulate briefly on our whole subject. First we will itemize in very general terms the main issues of part I.

1 First of all in historical terms we must recognize the disagreement that has occurred between associationism and its opponents. This starts with what we have called Naive Associationism being opposed by such views as those of the Würzburg School and the Gestalt School. Again, to put the matter in very general terms this led to the emergency of a more sophisticated associationism (e.g. Tolman) where the importance of the issues such as set, and other dynamic interactionary features were seen to play a vital part in learning.

2 The terms in which learning theorists tackled the higher cognitive processes still though remained unsatisfactory, and this has led to more sophisticated attempts to provide at least an appropriate framework in which thinking and the like could be described and studied. This implies the use of theories and models. At the same time we wish now to place much more emphasis on the part played by language in cognitive affairs.

3 The overall method used is essentially one of proceeding by

stages from informal to more precise definition of terms, always insisting on the contextual nature of such definitions.

4 Perception has been considered briefly and some people will feel that in our efforts we have underestimated its importance. The truth is that we are bound in our search for rigorous simplifications to distort and, by definition, oversimplify. However, matters of recognition and pattern recognition in particular, occur implicitly throughout our text.

5 Adaptation with a store provides a basis for learning. Motivation, through drives and needs, both learned and innate, provide the feedback and selective reinforcement. It is assumed that the ability to formulate concepts, to make generalizations and to test these hypotheses (generalizations) leads to the higher cognitive processes. Tolman's type of learning theory seems best able, of the older learning theories, to accommodate these features. Since then other theories have emerged[1] which bear, on the whole, a closer resemblance to the more philosophically orientated approach[2] to such matters.

6 The theory language or theoretical framework proposed in this monograph as background, is still essentially the same as the framework formulated by George and Handlon. We start with such concepts as beliefs, expectancies, motives, which are modified by feedback from changing needs and changing goals, and so on and so forth.

7 We need to say the obvious too: a human being is made up of a memory store—short and long term. He processes information by collating and classifying sensory inputs from internal and external sources, and on this internally stored material he works, and is supplied with data as needed (data retrieval), and this is all bound up with the processes of recognition and recall. He is able to manufacture concepts and generalizations or hypotheses (induction) and to reason from such bases (deduction). Naturally since language is used for

[1] J. A. Olds, High functions of the nervous system, *Ann. Rev. Physiol.*, *21*, 381–407; G. A. Miller, E. Galanter and K. H. Pribram, *Plans and the Structure of Behaviour*, Holt, 1960; K. W. Spence, *Behavior Theory and Conditioning*, Yale University Press, 1958; C. E. Osgood, *Method and Theory in Experimental Psychology*, Oxford University Press, 1953; O. H. Mowrer, Learning Theory and the Symbolic Process, New York, Wiley, 1960.

[2] C. W. Morris, *Signs, Language and Behavior*, Prentice Hall, 1946; F. H. George and J. H. Handlon, Towards a general theory of behavior, *Methodos*, 7, 25–44; F. H. George and J. H. Handlon, A language for perceptual analysis, *Psychol. Rev.*, *64*, 14–25.

communication it must also play a vital part in the information processing.

In part II, of course, we have taken further these higher cognitive features and tried to formulate precise models in computer program form, and we must try to show how they hang together to give something like a coherent picture of a type of thinking process. We do not of course say this is exactly how human beings process information, we are merely supplying possible models which we know 'do the trick', as far as we have gone so far, and it remains to show that they do the trick in the same way as human beings do it.

There are of course numerous difficulties over comparison between the models, even when integrated into one large model, and human behaviour itself. These are matters for debate and opinion and apply in any case to any theories or experimental evidence purporting to be about human behaviour.

2 A Complete Picture

At the time of writing, no program for the computer has been written which actually performs, in one continuous process all the steps discussed in Chapters 5–8. But let us try to clarify the picture achieved so far and pave the way for such programs. The vital processes explicitly discussed are:

1 Concept Formation.
2 Hypothesis Formation, which brings up the whole question of induction.
3 Deduction.
4 Language.

Clearly we are envisaging a process here where, say, a problem occurs and concepts and hypotheses are called up, and new concepts and hypotheses formulated if needed, and then the problem is solved or not as a result of a mixture of induction and deductive processing interspersed with conversation and data retrieval. This last is needed as a source of information since "other people" and books, etc need to be "spoken to" or "read from" in most cases.

Vital to this processing is recognition, and although we indicated some part of what recognition does in the processing, it is certain that a vast amount more needs to be done. Even the largest computer, on a multi-programming basis and using outside storage, needs recognition programs all the time. For example, our program ultimately is to say in effect "this sort of problem (situation) calls for a t-test, or factor analysis" and here one can think of the application of any of dozens of corporately developed techniques each of which needs to be called up by a recognition process. It is fairly obvious that not many human beings can do this at all, and none can do it for *all* such techniques—hence the age of specialization. Such a central program as is needed would be almost exclusively, in effect, a reference library.

The last comment should serve as a reminder that if we use such computer techniques to solve problems in practice, they too would be highly specialized; the dangers then are—as with human beings who are specialized—that vital information might be overlooked.

A further point is of course that we are assuming that the mere collecting of information and the ability to use that information in a sort of simple maze-running manner is easily available. We have not attempted to show how the higher cognitive behaviour emerges from such simple stimulus-response type of behaviour, this must at some stage be done.

Perhaps it should be said bluntly that any attempt to program the full range of human behaviour is quite beyond us at the moment and in this book we are only scratching the surface of what we take to be the central problem of thinking.

We can put together a variety of different program blocks to form various different automata which can be used for experiment of comparison. For example a Kochen or an Amarel model in program form could be placed in our *concept* and *hypothesis* blocks in Figure 1 which shows a block diagram of our model in very general form:

Figure 1, has an input which accepts stimuli if appropriately motivated, or in a sufficient state of awareness, and this is perceived (interpreted) or recognized more often (interpreted as familiar) and then concepts, hypotheses and the like are called up and used *on a whole variety of levels of generality*. They are all subject to the motivational state of the system (which includes here what we call emotions in people) and responses, plans or strategies, etc are all so affected.

The expectancies are the finished alternative models of action, which are analyzed for expected out-come and risk, prior to being acted upon.

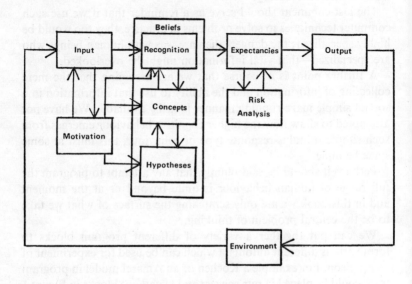

Fig. 1   A General block diagram of our Model

Risk Analysis is yet another block of programs which we need to write in order to even partially complete our picture. The methods here are fairly familiar[1] and involve an assessment of probably outcomes and such matters as minimizing regret; as in so many other of the examples discussed, it may be assumed that the average human being operates on a far more complicated basis than this suggests. However these at least included, as in the case of Amarel and Kochen, so here a whole range of strategies can be the subject of Experimentation. We shall not attempt to discuss these matters further, but it must be emphasized that they are matters that need the most detailed analysis and it is hoped that such an analysis will be provided in the near future.

Closely related to the sort of decision processing of Hurwicz, Wald, etc is that of Ward Edwards[2] with his work on Bayesian decision taking. His experiments show clearly the great advantage to be gained in a man-machine relationship where the processing of the data with a view to extracting the best outcome is better done by the machine than the man. We should also mention here the work of Suppes and Atkinson.[3]

Figure 2 shows a flow chart which carries a little more detail as to the programming situation; it is of course still very much more general than that need for detailed program writing. It does deal in the blocks discussed in Part II, but again all sorts of interchange of modules are both possible and desirable.

This field of "subjective" assessment is manifestly complex and we are hoping in this book only to provide methods for getting to grips with it through the medium of a computer.

Indeed we have arrived at the point where such large scale models need to be worked on in a context of feedback, so that they are to some extent self-correcting, and will alternatively become wholly so.

It would have been satisfactory to have written a book describing such 'complete' automata's behaviour, but that is the very *next* stage of the evaluation of Cybeneties in the field of human simulation.

Before leaving this very brief discussion of decision taking, we

1 R. M. Thrall, C. H. Coombs and R. L. Davis, *Decision Processes*, New York: Wiley, 1954; R. C. Jeffrey, *The Logic of Decision*, McGraw Hill, 1965.
2 Ward Edwards and Amos Tversky, *Decision Making*, Harmondsworth: Penguin, 1967. See also references in this book to further work by Ward Edwards and associates.
3 P. Suppes and R. C. Atkinson, *Markov Learning Models for Multiperson Interactions*, Stanford University Press, 1960.

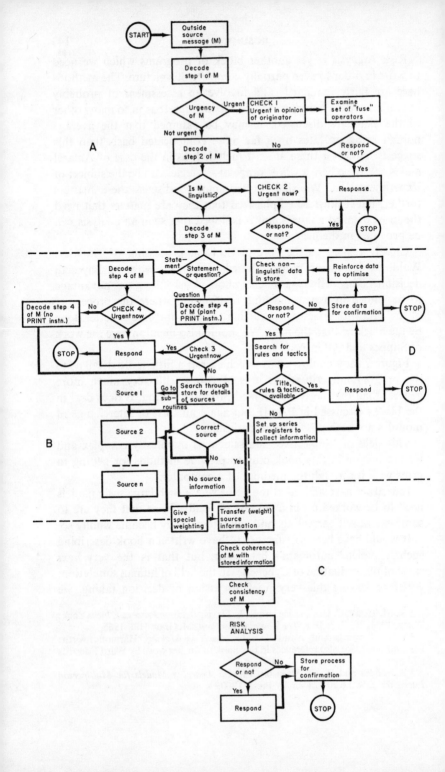

should make a few more general comments.[1] There is still a large gap between game theoretic models viewed as a normative mathematical undertaking and the psychological details of how people actually behave. If we think of *utilities* as being our choice of ends, and *probabilities* being our assessment of successful outcomes, these are interconnected with means and their probabilities in the means-ends assessments. People in practice often make what appear to be bad decisions and we want to know why.

The question is often asked as to why the same person in much the same situation will often make a different decision. In fact, of course, two occurrences are never identical, and even if seen to be, the assessment of previous success, to say nothing of human curiosity, will, or may, encourage a change of decision. Indeed where the situation is the other way round, we often find people acting in what were previously successful ways when the situation has been changed.

3 Oddities of Thinking

We are taking the view that thinking is a data processing activity which is mainly logical and involves language and its use. We are thinking of emotions as effectively interfering with these processes although the emotions have a vital survival function analogous to a "fuse box". It is obvious that emotions and their complex interaction with the "data processing" activities are vital to an understanding of human behaviour. We are not primarily concerned with this problem. Let us though make the following general statements:

1 Emotions spring from organic bodily states whose primary role was to fit the animal or human for likely activity, especially in emergency.

2 Internal emotional states have external signs which we have learned to associate with them.

3 A part of what we mean by motivation is emotionally determined, since states of fear, anger, etc clearly motivate and help to direct behaviour.

4 Emotional features must ultimately be brought into a program, either directly by chemical (or colloidal-chemical) means or indirectly by mathematical functions.

Let us pass on quickly to consider some other of what we have

1 H. H. Price, *Thinking and Experience*, London: Hutchinson, 1953.

called 'oddities'. First of all, we will discuss imaging, and then its relation to consciousness.

4   Consciousness and Imaging

This section is mainly speculative and refers to the sort of computer programming models we have been discussing in this book.

If, as seems necessary, a computer program is to show the property of being proof against "bluffs" or indeed if it is to have the capacity to change its own goals or subgoals, it must, as we mentioned earlier, carry an internal model of its environment. This internal model must involve calibrations of the reliability of information sources, details about people and things, both in particular and in general terms.

As far as bluffing is concerned this involves the need to analyze the *motives* in other external human-like sources. It is, of course, obvious that these are complicated probabilistic activities and are likely to be unreliable, but this is not our present concern as such. What we are concerned with is the fact that having an internal model of the external environment also entails a model of the people in it and their characteristics. It also involves a model of the "self", i.e. the program must contain some representation of itself. This self-representation can be picturesquely thought of as being like the bear on the label of the treacle tin; he is holding a treacle tin in the picture and on it is a bear holding a treacle tin and so on. This is surely one aspect of consciousness and self-awareness.

The fact of having images is another aspect. You can be aware of the non-present[1] and this conceptualization process is the process of having images, even though those images are associated with labels (words, etc).

You can reconstruct a previous sensory experience, at least in part, and this is surely the process of internal stimulation of data in store, which can also be recombined into "non-actual patterns". The equivalent process in our program scheme is the ability to reconstruct models of the environment as they are needed. Computers *could* have all of their stores information reconstructed, but the reconstruction may only be partial because some detail is lost. The losing of the detail may itself be a result of the process of formulating hypotheses.

[1] H. H. Price, *Thinking and Experience*, London, Hutchinson, 1953.

Galton's[1] famous questionnaire studies of imagery serve as a reminder if any were needed of the flimsiness of images for most people eidetic images are strongest in young people, and imagery generally is thought to be weakest in those regularly handling abstract ideas.

Individual differences now rear their heads and we must accept the fact that there is a tremendous variety in people's internal "mental operations" or as we have thought of it, data processing. The main point is that we shall think of images and special features such as synaesthesia as being a by-product of the transferrences, reverberatory circuits and the like that occur in data processing.

The above brief discussion is in a sense no help in itself, it is simply an attempt, and a brief one at that, to hint that all sorts of apparently diverse activities and oddities could be brought into line with the processing approach that we have been following in this monograph.

5 Information Processing

This monograph lays no claim to completeness, so we have not attempted to describe approaches to thinking by such well known people as Wertheimer, Spearman, Vygotsky and Piaget[2] among many others; nor in particular have we attempted to deal with the Factor Analysis approach.[3]

We have, in effect, been solely concerned with thinking as information processing. We are trying to follow in the footsteps of Newell, Shaw and Simon[4] when they laid down the following criteria:

1 A control system consists of memories, which contain symbolized information and which are interconnected by various ordering relations.

2 A number of primitive information processes operate on the information and each such operation is a function of a specific physical mechanism.

[1] F. Galton, *Inquiries into Human Faculty*, London: Macmillan, 1883.

[2] M. Wertheimer, *Productive Thinking*, New York: Harper, 1945; C. Spearman, *The Nature of Intelligence and the Principles of Cognition*, London: Macmillan, 1923; L. S. Vygotsky, *Thought and Language*, New York: Wiley, 1962; J. H. Piaget, *Judgement and Reasoning of the Child*, New York: Harcourt Brace, 1928.

[3] H. H. Harmon, *Modern Factor Analysis*, University of Chicago Press, 1960.

[4] A. Newell, J. C. Shaw and H. A. Simon, Elements in a theory of human problem solving, *Psychol. Rev.*, 1958, *65*, 151–66.

3 These processes can be combined into programs by rules.

They say, of course, a great deal more than this, but this is their starting point. We would wish to add that for us:

4 Concepts are either formed or attained as new experience occurs and from old experience stored but necessarily processed.

5 Hypotheses can be constructed from concepts—old and new—as external circumstances demand, as in problem solving, or as occurs conceptually in rumination.

6 Programs can be written to simulate 4 and 5 and the use of heuristic methods is automatically born. The goals provide the selective feedback which "drives" the organism or program.

7 Internal models of the environment occur and all of these can be described linguistically. So that we have stored data *and* its verbal description, and the relation between the two are semantic rules.

8 The descriptions are, or can be hierarchical, so that they can lead to explanations at many levels of generality and they can be self-referential.

9 Models that refer to humanlike beings in the environment must refer to likely motive as well as reliability.

10 The fact of internal models which are also self-referential is the basis for goal-changing or goal-modification, and is probably, with the neurological fact of imaging, the basis of consciousness and self-awareness.

We shall not pursue this matter any further. The story as it has been told in this book is about models—computer models in modular form—for the central, or some of the central, features of thinking. We hope they suggest a point of view which might be useful for others to follow up.

APPENDIX I

A SAMPLE LIP

PROGRAM FOR QUESTION-AND-ANSWER PROCEDURE AND DATA RETRIEVAL

Question (S_1) = IOMzY stop $\equiv$ 10(012)(101)(025)(999) where stop is coded 999 and the question, in effect, means 'Can computer C, play noughts and crosses?'

PROGRAM	COMMENTS
$D_1(S_1)$	$D_1(S_1)$, $D_2(S_1)$ etc as input arrives
$D_2(S_1)$	
$- - -$	
A_1 COP $D_1/B_1/A_2$	$B_1(S_1)$ Copy of S_1 in data section
A_2 COM $D_2/B_2/A_6$	$B_2(O)$ See if D_2 is empty
A_3 COP $D_2/B_3/A_4$	Copy rest of S_1 into data $B_3(D_2)$
A_4 COM $D_3/B_2/A_7$	Check if anything in D_3
A_5 $-$	Instruction need if $B_2 \not\equiv D_3$
A_6 $-$	
A_7 ADD $B_1/B_4/B_5$	$B_4(90 \ldots 0)$, $B_5(B_1$ and $B_4)$
A_8 TOV $B_5/A_9/A_{10}$	$B_5(00012101025)$ *Check digit* 1
A_9 COP $D_1/C_{200}/A_{11}$	$C_{200}(S_1)$ This could happen anytime
A_{10} $-$	If non-linguistic, use new procedure
A_{11} COP $B_5/B_6/A_{12}$	$B_6(00012101025)$; $B_5 = B_6$
A_{12} SHL $B_5/1/A_{13}$	Move S_1 (1 eliminated) one space left

PROGRAM	COMMENTS
A_{13} ADD $B_5/B_4/B_6$	To check digit 2
A_{14} TOV $B_6/A_{30}/A_{15}$	Check digit 2—question
A_{15} ADD $B_5/B_7/B_8$	Eliminate 9 from most sig. place
A_{16} COP $B_7/C_{201}/A_{17}$	$B_7(10 \ldots 0)$, B_8 (00012101025)
A_{17} SHR $B_8/6/A_{18}$	B_8 (0 \ldots 012)
A_{18} COM $B_8/C_1/A_{35}$	
A_{19} COM $B_8/C_2/A_{40}$	Check digits 3, 4 and 5 of S_1
A_{20} COM $B_8/C_3/A_{45}$	
$- - -$	
A_{30} $-$	If not a question use alternative procedure
$- - -$	
A_{35} $-$	Check K, not used here
$- - -$	

A_{40} SHL $B_8/6/A_{41}$
A_{41} COP $B_8/C_{201}/A_{42}$ $C_{201}(100120 \ldots 0)$
A_{42} SHL $B_6/5/A_{43}$ Eliminate 5 most sig. digits from B_6
A_{43} SHR $B_6/5/A_{50}$ $B_6(00000101025)$

$- - -$

A_{45} $-$ Check 0, not used here

PROGRAM	COMMENTS

A_{50} SHR $B_6/3/A_{51}$ $B_6(z)$
A_{51} COM $B_6/C_1/A_{61}$
A_{52} COM $B_6/C_2/A_{66}$
A_{53} COM $B_6/C_3/A_{71}$
A_{54} COM $B_6/C_4/A_{76}$
A_{55} COM $B_6/C_5/A_{81}$ Check digits 6, 7 and 8 of S_1, and
A_{56} COM $B_6/C_6/A_{86}$ identify z
A_{57} COM $B_6/C_7/A_{91}$
A_{58} COM $B_6/C_8/A_{96}$
A_{59} COM $B_6/C_9/A_{101}$

$- - -$

A_{61} $-$ If next symbol K

$- - -$

A_{66} $-$ If next symbol M

$- - -$

A_{71} $-$ If next symbol 0

$- - -$

A_{76} $-$ If next symbol operator 4

$- - -$

A_{81} $-$ If next symbol operator 5

$- - -$

PROGRAM	COMMENTS

A_{86} $-$ If next symbol operator 6

$- - -$

A_{91} $-$ If next symbol operator 7

$- - -$

A_{96} $-$

$- - -$

A_{101} SHL$/B_6/3/A_{102}$ Put z back in position
A_{102} ADD$/C_{201}/B_6/C_{201}$ Put z in C_{201}

A_{103} SHL $B_5/8/A_{104}$
A_{104} SHR $B_5/8/A_{105}$ B_5(Y)
A_{105} COM $B_5/C_1/A_{130}$ ⎫ Search for Y
A_{106} COM $B_5/C_2/A_{135}$ ⎪
A_{107} COM $B_5/C_3/A_{140}$ ⎪
A_{108} COM $B_5/C_4/A_{145}$ ⎪
A_{109} COM $B_5/C_5/A_{150}$ ⎪
A_{110} COM $B_5/C_6/A_{155}$ ⎬
A_{111} COM $B_5/C_7/A_{160}$ ⎪
A_{112} COM $B_5/C_8/A_{165}$ ⎪
A_{113} COM $B_5/C_9/A_{170}$ ⎪
A_{114} COM $B_5/C_{10}/A_{174}$ ⎭ Y identified
- - -

PROGRAM	COMMENTS
A_{130} – - - -	If next symbol K
A_{135} – - - -	If next symbol M
A_{140} – - - -	If next symbol 0
A_{145} – - - -	If next symbol operator 4
A_{150} – - - -	If next symbol operator 5
A_{155} – - - -	If next symbol operator 6
A_{160} – - - -	If next symbol operator 7
A_{165} – - - -	If next symbol operator 8
A_{170} – - - -	If next symbol operator z

A_{174} COP $C_{10}/A_{188}/A_{175}$
A_{175} COP $D_2/B_9/A_{176}$
A_{176} COM $B_9/C_1/A_{172}$ *Search* repeated until stop C_{11} (stop)
- - -   These instructions not included, as the
          technique of searching is already clear.

PROGRAM	COMMENTS
A_{203} STO/O/O/O	5 words only
A_{204} TRA/B_2/C_{107}/A_{206}	Test C_{107}
A_{205} PRI/1/C_{107}/A_{207}	6 words only
A_{206} STO/O/O/O	Stop
A_{207} – – –	and so on until last word is printed out of C_{111} (instructions not all given)
Statements $S_2 \equiv$	11(011)(012)(071)(021)(071)(022)
$S_3 \equiv$	11(011)(012)(012)(071)(023)(071)(022)
$S_4 \equiv$	11(011)(012)(012)(072)(021)(012)(072) (022)(011)(012)(071)(023)(012)(071)(024)

L

APPENDIX II

A SECOND LIP PROGRAM IN SKELETON FORM

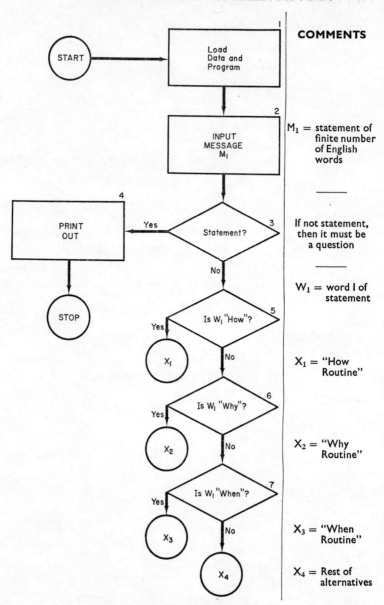

The Recognition Procedure

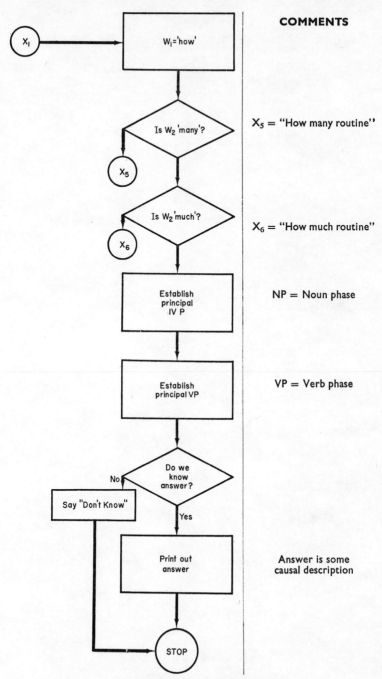

The Syntactical Procedure

APPENDIX III

$\alpha, \beta, \ldots, \gamma$ Individuals

A, B, ..., N as *Operators*

A, B, ..., N, also as addresses for storage locations in the computer

A, B, ..., N, to represent *events*

a, b, ..., n, as *classes*

a, b, ..., n, as contents of locations in computer store

A (a), B (b), ... item a is in location A, item b is in location B, ...

x, y, ..., w properties, or constants

Or $\cup$, V, O

And $\cap$, ., A

Not ~, N

A (x) F (x) means "for all x, function f holds"

E (x) F (x) means "there is at least one x for which function f holds"

C class membership

$\equiv$ Equivalence

if ... then $---\rightarrow$, $\supset$, I

α, ϕ, ζ, Locations in space

H_1, H_2, 11, H Hypotheses $\equiv$ Henrishes

$\leftarrow$ is implied by

C is contained in

B Boolean Algebra or calculus of classes

P Propositional Calculus

R Calculus of Relations

F Functional Calculus

$\rangle$ greater than

$\langle$ less than

$\vdash$ is an accepted statement

INDEX

SUBJECT INDEX

NAME INDEX

Ach, N., 18
Amarel, S., 57, 74 et seq.
Ashby, W. R., 24
Atkinson, R. C., 143
Austin, G. A., 49, 50

Banerji, R. B., 31, 57, 60, 64, 65, 73, 76, 95
Barry, G., 23
Bartlett, Sir F. C., 45, 47, 51, 54
Bartley, S. H., 43, 44
Black, M., 93
Bohnert, H. G., 132
Booth, A. D., 116
Boring, E. G., 18
Braithwaite, R. B., 23
Bruner, J. S., 49, 50, 51
Burstall, R. M., 89
Bush, R., 56

Carnap, R., 36, 115
Chomsky, C., 129
Chomsky, N., 117, 131
Claparede, E., 16
Colin, A. J. T., 132
Coombs, C. H., 143

Darlington, J. L., 91, 132
Davis, R., L. 91, 132
Drever, J., 39, 43, 48
Dreyfus, H. L., 22, 44

Edmundson H. P., 116
Edwards W., 143
Estes, W. K., 56

Feigenbaum, E. A., 20, 76
Fitch, F. B., 23
Foder, A. J., 131
Forster, J. M., 132

Galanter, E., 49, 74, 139
Galton, F., 147
Gelerntner, H., 20
George, F. H., 24, 31, 34, 39, 43, 44, 48, 58, 59, 66, 78, 88, 91, 92, 93, 95, 98, 99, 107, 108, 109, 110, 115, 129, 131, 139
Gibson, J. J., 18, 43
Goodnow, J. J., 49, 50
Green, B. E., 129
Guthrie, E. R., 16

Handlon, J. H., 92, 139
Harlow, H., 53, 54
Harmon, H. H., 20, 147
Hayek, S. A., 38
Head, Sir H., 45
Hilgard, E. R., 33, 48
Hilpinen, R., 93
Hochberg, J., 43
Hovland, C. I., 32, 54, 57, 74, 76
Hull, G. L., 17, 23
Humphrey, G., 17
Hunt, E. B., 17, 32 33, 50, 54, 57, 74, 76

Kaplan, A., 107
Keen, G. B., 101
Kemeny, J. C., 133
Kochen, M., 57, 75, 76, 133
Köhler, I., 43
Köhler, W., 49
Körner, S., 31, 52, 53
Korzybski, A., 115
Kulpe, O., 19

Langfeld, H. S., 18
Laughery, K., 129
Levien, G., 110, 132
Lindsay, R. K., 130, 131
Locke, W. N., 116

165

GEORGE ALLEN & UNWIN LTD

Head Office
40 Museum Street, London W.C.1
Telephone: 01-405 8577

Sales Distribution and Accounts Departments
Park Lane, Hemel Hempstead Herts.
Telephone: 0442 3244

Athens: 7 Stadiou Street
Auckland: P.O. Box 36013, Northcote Central N.4
Barbados: P.O. Box 222, Bridgetown
Beirut: Deeb Building, Jeanne d'Arc Street
Bombay: 103/5 Fort Street, Bombay 1
Calcutta: 285J Bepin Behari Ganguli Street, Calcutta 12
Cape Town: 68 Shortmarket Street
Delhi: 1/18B Asaf-Ali Road, New Delhi 1
Hong Kong: 105 Wing On Mansion, 26 Hancow Road, Kowloon
Ibadan: P.O. Box 62
Karachi: Karachi Chambers, Mcleod Road
Madras: 2/18 Mount Road. Madras
Mexico: Villalongin 32, Mexico 5, D.F.
Nairobi: P.O. Box 30583
Philippines: P.O. Box 157, Quezon City D-502
Rio de Janeiro: Caixa Postal 2537-Zc-00
Singapore: 36c Prinsep Street, Singapore 7
Sydney: N.S.W.: Bradbury House, 55 York Street
Tokyo: C.P.O. Box 1728, Tokyo 100-91
Toronto: 81 Curlew Drive, Don Mills

BASIC PSYCHOANALYTIC CONCEPTS ON THE LIBIDO THEORY

Edited by DR HUMBERTO NAGERA

The libido theory is one of the major areas of interest in psycho-analysis. Freud's insights in this field have been widely applied and used by psychoanalysts, adult and child psychiatrists, psychologists, educationalists, experts on child development and social workers.

They have thrown light on the normal and abnormal aspects of sexual development from childhood to adulthood and on the role played by sexual development in neurotic disturbances. Further they have made possible an understanding of the complex field of sexual perversions. In this volume the reader will find twenty-four basic psychoanalytic concepts concerning the libido theory including oral erotism, anal erotism, phallic erotism, genital erotism, of oedipus complex of the girl, the oedipus complex on the boy, autoerotism, narcissism, masochism, sadism and bisexuality.

As in other volumes in this series, the historical development of each concept and references to Freud's works are clearly given so that students and scholars can pursue any aspect of special interest.

BASIC PSYCHOANALYTIC CONCEPTS ON THE THEORY OF DREAMS

Edited by DR HUMBERTO NAGERA

Dr Nagera and his collaborators (all analytically trained) from the Hampstead Child Therapy Clinic and Course (Director, Anna Freud) have isolated from Freud's work twenty-five basic concepts that they consider not only the corner stones of Freud's theory of dreams but fundamental pillars for the understanding of psychoanalytic theory generally. They include subjects such as dream sources, dream work, dream censorship, manifest content, latent content, condensation, displacement, symbolism, secondary revision and dream interpretation. They are presented in a condensed and concentrated manner containing all significant statements made by Freud at any point in his life on the subject of dreams, as well as tracing the historical development of his ideas wherever significant. References to the sources are given in all instances for the guidance of the student of psychoanalysis, the psychiatrist, the social worker, the psychologist or the scholarly minded reader.

LONDON: GEORGE ALLEN AND UNWIN LTD